# ICARUS
# REDEEMED
## A SCHIZOAFFECTIVE STORY

# ICARUS
# REDEEMED
## A SCHIZOAFFECTIVE STORY
### G.H. FRANCIS

LONE DRAGONFLY BOOKS
lonedragonflybooks.com

While the events in this book are true, the names of individuals
have been changed to protect their identities.

Cover illustration by Justin Schnarr
Book design by Maureen Cutajar

December 2015

ISBN 978-0996735025

*For my family, who provided support*
*and love throughout difficult times.*

# Prologue

In madness, every passageway, no matter how misguided, climbs toward salvation; in despair, every path, no matter how promising, leads to Hell. Having lived through three major, life-altering manic episodes, each resulting in institutionalization, and countless bouts of depression, I know this statement is true. I also know that madness and depression are part of me, but not all of me, and with work and dedication both can be managed. Being diagnosed with a mental illness felt like the end of my "normal" life, but it was really the beginning of a "different" life, a life that did not bury my sense of self—as it initially seemed—but instead taught me who I really am. In the end, it's not the clothes we wear, family we come from, or music we listen to that define us; it's the obstacles we overcome.

This is my second attempt to write this story. It is difficult to write, not only because it contains explicit details about embarrassing events in my life, but also because it forces me to look back on experiences I've attempted to suppress and memories I've attempted to forget. By returning to those memories, I reenter a dark and confusing cave I left behind several years ago, this time with a light to cast a new perspective on the twisted passageways I've traveled. I am afraid to write this book, but if I did not step back into that place of darkness, I would run the risk of forgetting who I was and, as a result, lose perspective on how far I've come. I hope that in some way, sharing my story will shed light on the path that I have travelled, and that others like me, and those who love them, will see that our experiences are not so different, and our accomplishments can be made together.

Even though I was there, it is sometimes difficult to remember my exact feelings at the time the events of this book occurred. However, I have access to primary resources to help take me back: interviews with close family members and friends who lived through these experiences, as well as my own poetry and journal entries from that time. I utilize this writing to express my journey, as these writings often occurred during or around my manic or depressive episodes and outline my thoughts and experiences at the time they were taken down. Although these excerpts do not necessarily represent who I am now, they represent who I was and, as the cave paintings of Lascaux show us something about the minds that created them, they will show you what was going on in my mind at the time they were created—during stability, depression, or madness.

The following is from my first attempt to write this book. Although I did not realize it at the time, it was written before my complete recovery, before attaining the outlook on life that I now hold. I include it now as a demonstration of the bipolar mind, which, given different moods, can write the same material in very different manners:

> I measure my bout with bipolar I in three distinct phases, each phase following a marked period of escalating thoughts culminating with a visit to a mental institution. Each phase has admittedly taken something from me and, while I'd like to tell you otherwise, I am today a shadow of the individual I once was.

Although I will refer to my illness as "bipolar" often in this text, and for eight years that was my diagnosis, my actual diagnosis is "schizoaffective disorder of the bipolar type," a cocktail of mental disorders with key elements of both schizophrenia and bipolar. Needless to say, I have come to have a deep understanding of both.

# 1

# Phoenix

When I lived in Phoenix, I had very little under-standing of bipolar disorder and, like many people, thought it was just a polite, socially acceptable way to refer to crazy people. I lived with two high school friends in an apartment in Tempe that overlooked I-10, which, when connected with I-17, divides Phoenix in two like the line that divides the black and white of the yin-yang symbol. Like many twenty-year-olds, I lacked direction – sleeping till noon, watching television for hours, sipping margaritas by the pool, attending classes sporadically, and toying with the notion of getting a job. I had about six thousand dollars when I moved out there, and it took me less than a year to spend the money on rent, food, and alcohol.

I was drunk most nights of the week and my roommates and I frequented a seedy, strip-mall bar that smelled and looked like the bottom of an ashtray. Like most respectable dives, this bar was the last stop for dozens of old alcoholics sharing stories about heroin-addicted sons who'd set their houses on fire or, pointing to tattoos made of ink that had turned blue and bled into their wrinkled skin, days in the Navy when men were men, and of brushes with long-forgotten famous people whose names we barely recognized. Because I had never known my grandfather, I was enthralled by these older men and listened to them with reverence, offering a listening ear to individuals who, it seemed, had long been struck mute by society. There was sadness in their eyes, a glassy reflection of white in the corner of their pupils that seemed to drop into a blackness that had been dug deeper by years of drinking, drugs, and regrets. Had things run their course in the manner that they were perhaps intended to, I would one day be like them.

Each evening we played darts, Golden Tee (a golf video game), and pool and listened to our favorite songs on the juke box, always making sure to play the song that ironically foreshadowed the future I would soon encounter - David Bowie's "Space Oddity" (Ground control to Major Tom). The song tells the story of an astronaut who, after reaching great heights, encounters a malfunction and, as a result, floats helplessly away from Earth and is lost in the vastness of space.

Each night was the same; we drank several pitchers of beer, and, when the bar closed at two in the morning, left reluctantly and stumbled home to our second-floor apartment.

Afternoons or late evenings (when I was drunk) I worked on a preachy book entitled *Running East*. It is the story of a guy who hates his job and decides to quit…with the inclusion of a hundred pages of philosophic nonsense, that's about it. I was very optimistic then, as twenty-year-olds tend to be, and believed I was writing the next great American novel. Unfortunately, upon later review of the completed book, that was very far from reality.

The following excerpt is the beginning of *Running East*. It is fueled by the drive for individuality that many of us feel, especially in our late teens and early twenties. During this time of optimism I created a character without individuality, a character that I considered the exact opposite of who I wanted to be; as the story progressed, I strove to turn him, Soco Killman, into the person I'd hoped to become. On the surface, the book was an adolescent rant about the commonness of the common man, the materialization of teenage angst, my Rage-Against-the-Machine-driven anger, my misanthropic hatred of society. In reality, it was a story filled with my own fears about what my life would become, about who I would become. Soco Killman was a fictional representation of myself, and *Running East* was a way of creating a fortification against the "common" life. Although many of its messages are immature, it has since served as a map from my young self, a warning about routine and acceptance. It is a photograph of a younger me. In the trajectory of my mental illness, *Running East* is really a starting point, the foundation of my thoughts, where everything began and where everything started to go wrong. The following is an excerpt:

## CHAPTER ONE: A NEW DAY

The dogwood trees, which laboriously twisted from square plots of earth checkering the city's concrete sidewalks, had remained green for an extended period despite the onset of an exceptionally bitter autumn. The local weathermen had attributed this seasonal rift to the bountiful spring and summer periods that had 'oversaturated' the trees with the necessities of life.

The phenomenon went unnoticed by most of the city's inhabitants, because the weather blips were dismissed as filler before the top story, the murder of Joseph Sapp, a twelve-year old boy who'd been held by a janitor in the basement of a large office building. The boy was eventually shocked to death by a cattle prod.

The reference to the "square plots of earth checkering the city's sidewalks" is a reference to grave plots and the story about the boy who was shocked to death introduces one of the story's main themes: society's killing of innocence. The mood and tone of the book were established in those first couple paragraphs, and little evolves from that point.

While it isn't Shakespeare, this book holds a special place in my heart, and it represents a time when my writing was fueled by a belief that I had something important to say, that my words had the ability to change the world, that people reading the book would drop their briefcases and wander off to a more peaceful, less capitalistic world.

2

# The Solo

I had decided to become a writer at the age of nineteen during a twenty-six day Outward Bound trip in Australia, an attempt to "start over" after two failed semesters of college. Outward Bound is an organization dedicated to outdoor adventure, specializing in teaching children and young adults the importance of the outdoors, as well as the ethics that come with them. A key element of the Outward Bound experience in Australia is the solo excursion into the outback: you are utterly alone from the time the instructor drops you off in the middle of the wilderness, till his return three days later. During these three solitary days of soul-searching beneath the canopy of foreign trees and amidst the sounds of foreign birds, I filled a small booklet with writings, philosophical quotes (which seem somewhat less philosophical these days), poetry, and the first few pages of *Running East*. Here is the first poem I ever wrote:

When it's sunny, God is smiling.

When it's cloudy, God is smiling.
When it's raining, God is smiling.
When it's snowing, God is smiling.

The product of a Jesuit, Catholic education, I held onto those beliefs after I graduated high school. These, I am convinced, would deeply affect me in the coming years and magnify during manic episodes. When my poetry wasn't overly sentimental or religious it bore the mildly sociopathic mark of Pink Floyd, my favorite band at the time.

Days pass slowly when you are alone in the woods, and minutes are endless. Every small movement of nature is experienced by the senses: the gust of wind felt coolly on the skin, the dry smell of summer rushing briskly by your nostrils, the trees bending, the leaves flickering and altogether sounding like water cascading over a small waterfall. I sat silent in one spot for long periods of time, meditating, or, from my small blanket, staring into the woods, thinking of the fast-paced world, of big cities, rushing cars, and billions of people, so distant from me that they seemed imaginary. This, I thought, is how we were meant to be. This is home. This is living.

As Thoreau says in *Walden*, "You only need sit still long enough in some attractive spot in the woods that all its inhabitants may exhibit themselves to you by turns." I spent much of my solo excursion watching a line of ants on a log, developing in my nineteen-year-old mind a distain for other humans, who seemed to create an equally long and pointless line of "human ants." It is here that the first misanthropic seeds were planted in my brain, seeds that would lead to isolation and delusions of grandeur, which, I believe, were a direct result of my desire to be more than an "ant." It is also possible that the seeds of a god-complex were developing, a thing that young children experience when they kill ants, taking lives at the slightest whim, and which (though I was not harming the ants) I was experiencing as an unseen observer of the ants' activities. Images of this experience would appear often in later writing.

In *Running East* there is a scene with Soco looking out his apartment window:

> He enjoyed watching people as they passed below because it gave him a quiet thrill to observe them and know they were unaware. In this omniscient state he was able to make a person whatever he wanted, so he made them kind, playful, and childlike.

And, a scene from a rocky overlook above a highway at night:

> *Below them, cars followed the concrete path like nocturnal ants with glowing halogen eyes.*

In my second book, *Lightbearer*, a novel written after my first manic episode and which was loosely based on those experiences, I would write about a circular mill, which is explained in the book as:

> An extremely rare occurrence that begins when a line of ants begins following another line of ants. Given the right scenario, with each ant instinctively following the

ant in front of it, a circular mill (or circle of ants) will
continue until there is a significant break in the line,
meaning enough ants die, thereby lessening the circum-
ference of the circle, or until an ant strays from the circle
and is followed by the rest of the mass.

When encountering a circlular mill of ants in a cave in
the Grand Canyon, the main character of *Lightbearer* uses
the flame from a lighter to force the ants from their endless
circular march. This, a reference to the title of the book, was
intended to be an allegory about the way people live their
lives and the wisdom, or 'flame', necessary to break them out
of their cycle. There is no doubt that I wanted to help people,
and I thought that busting them out of the jail of society, so
to speak, was the way to do it. I have since learned that most
people don't want or need that sort of help. However, deep
down I think we all struggle with thoughts of insignificance,
and in seeking purpose in our lives we are really saying,
"Look, I have the power to change things. I am significant."

Influenced by Walt Whitman, I would later write "On
Ants", a portion of which follows:

For you, minute vagrant, are the teacher of many things
Of courage, of strength, of community, of love
While not a one could stand to read the praises that I
    sing
To readers I say, not all teachers come from above.

Reading this poem now reminds me of how impressiona-
ble my young mind was then. My writing shifted based on

what I was reading, as though exploring the universe for a place to call my own, but always finding each place occupied.

During these three days alone in the outback, I also developed an aversion to material things, and began to reject society's typical notion of "success," as is demonstrated in this poem:

SUCCESS
A log on the fire
Feeding the flame
That burns through our hearts
And brightens our names
A light to the masses
Taking hope from the few
Leaving behind some gray worthless ashes.

And my hatred of society was developing quickly:

I despise society. Society kills the human spirit…Society is the beast that shapes and molds our minds until they are nothing.

These words make me cringe now, seeming childish, adolescent and naïve. They are the words of a scared boy, afraid to fail and afraid to succeed. These fears, I think, are held by many of us during late adolescence as we start college or work, choosing paths we will most likely follow for the rest of our lives, measuring the importance of happiness that comes from following the self against the importance of money and power, sometimes thinking both to be the same.

Since reading it in high school, I have always loved Robert Frost's "The Road Not Taken," and the last stanza has always seemed significant:

> I shall be telling this with a sigh
> Somewhere ages and ages hence:
> Two roads diverged in a wood, and I-
> I took the one less traveled by,
> And that has made all the difference.

I have often wondered why Frost chose to repeat the word 'I' in the last three lines, but I think now that he is trying to say that the decision was his own, that he, and no one else, influenced the path he traveled. It is like Sinatra singing, "I did it my way." Or could it be a stutter? A moment of uncertainty experienced during the retelling of the tale? Now, I'm not so sure.

While on my solo, influenced by this, the first thing I wrote that wasn't a poem was:

> Many would argue that life is a giant intersection with millions of different paths. I think life is an endless path, one direction leads to a life of following society and the other of following yourself. You can choose one or the other, no in between.

Things were more black and white then, and it wasn't until later in my life that I'd even consider the option of changing your path, but I think, ultimately, both paths run parallel to each other – one being the 'high' road, and one being the 'low' road - although these days I don't judge people based on the road they've chosen, and see things in a grayer light, arguing now that life is indeed a "giant intersection with millions of different paths." One of the greatest gifts in life is the freedom to choose your own path, and who am I to say your path is wrong. "To each their own," or so they say.

The black and white choice between society and self was the driving force behind *Running East,* and it fed my desire to lead an exceptional life. This desire would soon grow into madness, becoming completely unhinged during manic episodes.

I cannot say whether these thoughts are those of a "normal" individual; I can only tell you that these were the thoughts I was having at the time. As many well-wishers and therapists have told me in the past, "there is no such thing as normal," which, I believe, is true. However, after having lived a few years and known a few adolescents, I believe these thoughts were not out of the ordinary. The truth is I was relatively normal, as normal as any of us are when we're that age.

CHAPTER

# 3

# The Gates of Madness

After nine months in Phoenix, I looked into a curious ad for a "Martial Arts Instructor" in the newspaper and got the job (people still used newspapers to find jobs back then). I had no prior experience and was not paid for this job; instead I received free training in exchange for giving lessons to lower rankings students than myself. This was a method based on the "old system" of martial arts training, but I'm fairly certain it was just a way for my *sensei* to cut costs. As you can imagine, I quickly ascended through the belts until I was high-ranking enough to teach most classes. But, as I exemplified and more than a few karate masters have said, "the only thing belts are good for is keeping up your pants."

My *sensei* was an edgy, slick-white-haired, potbellied Jewish Vietnam vet with a love of bar-b-que ribs who reveled in his position of power and rarely left his office, allowing the instructors to carry out his most trivial chores, which we did obediently. That being said, he was a wise man – at least to my perception at the time – and he cared very much for his students and his instructors, with whom he adopted a tough love method of teaching.

After several months as a martial arts instructor I moved in with a new roommate with whom I frequently smoked marijuana. Soon I was smoking several times a day.

Although I had been smoking since the age of sixteen, the marijuana in Arizona seemed to have a strong effect on me, possibly due to additional chemicals that may have been added to increase the drug's potency. On one occasion I spent several minutes watching a police drama in which two officers were at the bottom of a fire escape arguing over the best way to enter a suspect's apartment. Upon walking in to the room, my roommate asked what I was doing; I looked at him and told him I was watching television. When I looked back at the television I saw only a black screen. It had been off the entire time.

On another occasion, while stoned and sitting in the pool hot tub on a ninety-five degree day, I listened as the bubbles "blooped" and "blopped" rhythmically and in song. I was so unsettled by this that I left the pool immediately, only realizing later that the music had originated from a rap song playing on a nearby radio.

I often think that these hallucinations were the precursor to the schizoaffective side of my disorder. Hearing countless times from psychiatrists, psychologists, and therapists that drugs have the ability to awaken dormant mental illnesses, I often wonder how things would have turned out if I had not smoked marijuana. In a way I resent the drug, making it the scapegoat of my disorder and blaming it for every wayward thought I've ever had. If I knew then what I know now, I would not have tried the drug, and even if it wasn't the trigger, it wasn't worth the risk.

Instructing martial arts in the evening, I attended Arizona State University part-time during the afternoon, pursuing a degree in Psychology. Like most Psychology students, I diagnosed myself with every disorder discussed in class; I suppose I was right on one or two occasions.

Other than *sensei*'s frequent talk of his glory days when he picked fights in bars just to try out new martial arts techniques, hung out with the Hells Angels, and dated strippers, I recall two incidents vividly. The first incident occurred on a Saturday afternoon. *Sensei* called all the instructors into his office. We lined up in order of rank and stood in military stance – chest out, left hand holding right wrist at the waist, right hand folded into a tight fist. Behind *sensei*'s desk on a table was an uzi with a long black clip. "I want you all to know," he said in his gravelly tough-guy voice, "that I was visited by an old friend yesterday. His name is Apache and he's a Hells Angel who was just released from prison," he ran his palm across his cat's spine and up its tail, rubbing his fingers together afterwards so that the shed fur floated toward the carpet. "Needless to say, Apache and I have unsettled business. He sat in that chair there and I was here and I placed a gun in the middle of the desk and said to him, 'if you want to kill me, grab the gun and kill me, but if I get to it first, I'm going to kill you.' Apache looked at the gun and then at me, then he stood up and left the office," *sensei* rocked his head to the side like a drunken Stevie Wonder—

he often did this. "I don't trust him, so I want you to be aware."

I was very thrilled at the time and felt exhilarated at the sight of the gun, becoming very serious about life for a while. Looking back on the story, I'm fairly certain it was made up, but that's the kind of person my *sensei* was. He probably thought it was teaching us some sort of lesson, although I can't imagine what that would be.

On another occasion we stood in sensei's office and he said, "No matter who you are, somebody will hate you just because you are who you are." This, I have since realized, is very good advice, but at the time I was very naïve and the statement stuck and began to deeply affect my interpersonal relationships, as from that point on I assumed that nobody liked me. This eventually developed into a much stronger paranoia.

I suppose that's how it starts for all of us with mental disorders, just a small statement that taps into a part of us that others don't have, taking us somewhere that others never have to go, making us think thoughts that most will never fully understand, no matter how we try to explain them. It's like trying to explain the feel of a cold winter day to someone who has lived in a tropical, one-season climate their whole life; they understand the concept of cold, as they have felt a range of temperatures, some cooler than others, but they can never fully understand *that* kind of cold without actually feeling it on their skin. People understand that there are good days and bad days when it comes to mood, but those of us with mental disorders often live in the extreme cold or extreme hot climates, although much of our lives are lived in the temperate zone that most people are used to.

That summer I returned to Maryland for a few weeks, driving my '91 Honda Accord cross-country with Nick, my friend of thirteen years. We stopped at Carlsbad Caverns in New Mexico, where we attempted to enter the caves at night. Everything locked up for the evening, we jumped the first ten-foot wrought-iron gate and descended a zigzagging concrete path leading into the gaping mouth of the caverns, which seemed large enough to fit half a football field in, out of which flowed the black silhouettes of countless bats.

As you near the entrance to the caverns, the path travels through a bored-out tunnel in the rock and into the inner caverns. Here, outside the tunnel, is an impassable gate. Our adventuring at an end, we returned the way we had come; although I still wonder if a part of me didn't pass through that gate and continue into the absolute darkness.

Nick cut his hand while jumping back over the wrought-iron gate. We camped that evening in our sleeping bags in the desert three hundred feet from a restroom, which we could smell over the arid, dry-clay earth.

After Carlsbad we stayed in a hostel in San Antonio, where we traveled along the river walk, a man-made canal lined with touristy restaurants and shops, and got our pictures taken in front of the Alamo. Then we got drunk and took pictures of each other pretending to drive a police boat that was docked at one end of the canal.

A day of driving brought us to New Orleans and to the India House, a hostel that looked as though it was straight out of the '60s, located just outside the main city. The walls of the India House were covered in photographs of guests who stuck out their tongues at the camera or hugged or kissed each other, or slugged beer or liquor. The kitchen was small and painted brightly with a mural of the sun, hearts, trees, birds, etc. and it smelled like smoke and alcohol. Out back there was a courtyard and two dormitory buildings. We stayed in a bunk bed in a dormitory filled with about nine other bunk beds and eighteen other scruffy, smelly, and frequently drunk travelers.

After we settled in, we returned to the kitchen and began drinking beer, sitting at the kitchen table and conversing with the unique travelers and listening to the occasional outburst from someone whose food had been taken from the refrigerator.

I first saw her sitting on a stool by the pay phone that hung from the wall at the end of the kitchen table. She had black hair and was with a friend. The friend, a tall blond-haired girl with a down-to-earth rich-girl look, sat on one side of the phone. I watched out of the corner of my eye as the black-haired girl answered the telephone with an Irish accent and then relayed to everybody that a certain person was wanted on the phone. This message echoed throughout the hostel until, a few moments later, the individual emerged. Nick, who is much more outgoing than I, began speaking with the two girls, who were students from the UK traveling across the United States. The girl with black hair was named Kate and she was from Ireland and was a Chemistry student at Oxford. Another young, drunken traveler joined the conversation and I was distracted for a few moments until I noticed the black-haired girl staring deeply at me with her green eyes. That fateful stare would haunt me for many years, creating an obsession that that time and time again drew me deeper into madness.

We spent the remaining two days in constant contact with the girls from the UK and drank with them each evening, and I have sour memories of them beating Nick and me in a game of pool, as well as hazy memories of leaving a Bourbon Street bar as the sun rose in the east. I had, as far as my young mind knew, fallen in love with Kate, but only had the courage to speak with her when I was drunk.

We returned late one evening from the bars. The night was humid and warm. Not tired, we sat on the wooden, Victorian-style front porch of the India House with our legs dangling over the porch's edge as we stared toward the stars. Kate told me that she liked Chemistry because it could be used to explain anything and, because I was reading about Einstein's Theory of Relativity at the time, I asked her how Chemistry figured into relativity. Not only did she know what relativity was, but she succinctly responded to the question. Although I was able to hold my own, due to the fact I was discussing things I had read six hours earlier, I was incredibly intimidated by her, and from that point on I was always trying to impress her with my knowledge of things that smart people like.

On the third evening we stayed up all night so that we could see the girls off when their taxi arrived at five a.m. I remember very little from that night, only that we lay on couches watching television. We did not speak and the entire time it felt as though a small candle were lit inside my heart, and the hot air it let off was slowly filling my heart and making it expand to an unnatural and unhealthy size. A strange sensation, especially considering we had never even kissed.

The sky was turning from black to navy when we hugged goodbye, but not before I'd gotten Kate's email address.

For the final leg of our trip Nick and I camped on a sandy beach beside a lake in the Great Smokey Mountains. We built a miniature city out of pebbles and small stones, complete with streets, houses, and a coliseum and that evening we got high and used the coliseum as our fire pit, dancing around our flaming arena while pretending to play the flute *a la* Nero. Another evening we lay on our backs on the beach and stared at the myriad stars composing the Milky Way, which swept majestically across the vista of the evening sky, the stars so numerous you'd think they were glinting grains of white sand in a deep, blue ocean.

Two lights approached on the water, one blue and one white, and, despite Nick's lack of concern, I was convinced the lights were from a police ship and that the cops onboard were going to arrest us. We fled into the woods and watched from the trees as the boat shone its spotlight on the beach, sat for a few minutes, and then moved on.

The developing paranoia is apparent as I look back on that incident, and everything seems to fit perfectly in place, the disorder becoming a skin mole that always seems to have been there, innocently benign until the day it turned malignant.

After a two-week stay in Maryland, I drove back across the country by myself to return to Phoenix, where, after the 4 or 5 day return trip, life picked up where it had left off. I still worked as a martial arts instructor and I still went to Arizona State University part-time. The only difference was that I soon began emailing Kate.

The first email was rather awkward, as we'd rarely talked when I wasn't drunk and I really didn't know that much about her, aside from the fact that she was studying Chemistry at Oxford and she was from Ireland. She told me about the rest of her trip in the United States, about her time in San Antonio and San Francisco, and I told her about the rest of my trip. Weeks passed between each email.

After Kate returned to school, we began emailing several times a week; I checked my email numerous times each day in hopes of hearing from her. Our friendship continued to develop on a fairly superficial level until September, when I began researching Nostradamus. This was the official beginning of my decline into madness.

Things move rapidly during manic episodes, and it is difficult to describe an episode without allowing the progression of thoughts to snowball out of control. It is my intention to simulate this process, so that you, who may never experience a manic episode, can better see how the mind is affected. Please approach it with an open mind, with the understanding that the thoughts were real to me. Imagine yourself in a world where these things are true, and you will understand the fear, confusion, and perhaps euphoria of a manic episode. What I've learned from the experiences explained in this book is that reality is defined by the individual; there is no such thing as a universal reality. Allow yourself to make my reality yours, and we will make this journey together. I was alone when I first made this journey.

Since reading about the Theory of Relativity I had become obsessed with time and spent a lot of time thinking about its truthfulness. Eventually, I believed that time does not necessarily occur in a linear fashion, one moment after another, but rather it was possible that all of time occurred at once. If this were true, there would be no past or future, only the present, and although our perceived present constantly changed, the actual present stayed the same. Therefore, it would be possible to tell the future if one merely reinterpreted the present. These thoughts made sense at the time and eventually became fact, although only to me. This is how all madness must begin, with a simple thought that makes sense only to the mind that created it. There was no stopping it; it was inevitable. If it wasn't that thought, it would have been another.

Parts of this theory make sense, as I could accurately predict the future by reinterpreting the present, in a big-picture kind of way. For example, I believe a war will be occurring in one hundred years and there will be starvation and death in the world. Miracles aside, I'll, unfortunately, probably be fairly accurate. That being said, I wondered if Nostradamus could have divined a more elaborate system to reinterpret the present for future times.

There are many stories about the powers of Nostradamus. According to one, Nostradamus was once asked by the owner of a castle in which he stayed the fate of a black pig and a white pig, and Nostradamus said that the white pig would be eaten by a wolf and they would eat the black pig. Seeking to discredit the seer, the castle owner ordered the white pig slaughtered and prepared for dinner. However, while being prepared the meat was taken by a wolf cub that was kept in the castle, so the cook slaughtered and prepared the black pig. At dinner, the castle owner accused Nostradamus of being wrong in his prediction, stating that they were currently eating the white pig, but the seer insisted they were eating the black pig. The cook was questioned and the truth was revealed.

Another supposed fact is that in 1700, nearly 150 years after his death, Nostradamus's tomb was opened and around his neck was found a necklace that said "1700."

The seer's prophecies are found in a book most commonly referred to as his book quatrains. The quatrains within the book are composed of stanzas of four lines each and look like lines of poetry. These lines do not rhyme as most poems of the time would have, and the lines oftentimes seem sporadic and unrelated to the next.

It was necessary for me to research Nostradamus' quatrains for this book, and the prospect of rereading those writings sent a surge of blood into my brain—the feeling I got when I felt I was losing control of my disorder. It always started as a mild headache, a tinge of heat behind either eye that most people would pass off as a result of too much sunlight. Soon the tinge became a voice that constantly second-guessed my words, thoughts, and movements, saying, "Is that what a sane person would do?" And, if things continued down that path, I couldn't answer because I didn't really know. Then I'd slip out for a while, disengaging from conversation, society, and reality and becoming angry and fearful, ready to curl into a ball and lay in bed for two weeks. Despite the urges to once again reinvestigate the quatrains, which still to this day hold the intrigue of truth for me, I move quickly past them.

The quatrains were written in the 1550s and contain hundreds of prophecies divided into centuries. Of the prophecies, several are considered to have come true.

Century 1, Quatrain 35 is suspected to have foretold the death of Henry II of France, who was killed during a jousting contest when the lance of a younger knight (the "young lion," as both men had lions on their shields) splintered when it struck Henry's helmet (his "golden cage"), one splinter piercing the king's eye, the other piercing his temple ("two wounds made one"). The following is the quatrain:

> The young lion will overcome the older one,
> On the field of combat in a single battle;
> He will pierce his eyes through a golden cage,
> Two wounds made one, then he dies a cruel death.

Century 2, Quatrain 57 is suspected of foretelling the French Revolution:

> Before the war comes, the great wall will fall,
> The King will be executed, his death coming too soon
>     will be lamented.
> (The guards) will swim in blood,
> Near the River Seine the soil will be bloodied.

Century 2, Quatrain 24, as well as several other quatrains, refers to Hister (Hitler)

> Beasts ferocious with hunger will cross the rivers,
> The greater part of the battlefield will be against Hister.
> Into a cage of iron will the great one be drawn,
> When the child of Germany observes nothing.

On September 10, 2001, when I was reading the quatrains, I thought nothing of this:

In the year 1999 and seven months
The Great King of Terror will come from the sky,
He will bring back to life the great king of the Mongols
Before and after the God of war reigns happily.


The following morning at 6:00 a.m., I was awakened by a call from Nick, who told me the World Trade Center had been attacked. I turned on the television, watched the footage we have all seen, and several hours later I was sitting in the Department of Motor Vehicles paying off a registration violation, watching the same footage amidst an ocean of silence. I went through the rest of the day as numbly as anyone else.

That evening I reread the previous quatrain. It wasn't precise, about two years off, but it seemed highly relevant to the horrors America was experiencing during that moment. At that point I was certain that Nostradamus could predict the future and I was determined to discover how. I do not know if it was the stress of the catastrophe that set me off, or if it was a coincidence, but from that point on I slipped further into mania.

The line "He will bring back to life the great king of the Mongols" created a train of thought that was deepened by Nostradamus's letter to his son, which I will talk about later. Having never considered reincarnation before, I began to think about the return of old souls in new bodies, and the possibility that souls are cyclical, returning with the same basic beliefs, but with different faces and names than their previous reincarnations.

I reread every quatrain each evening when I arrived home at 10:30 and did not share my newfound obsession with anybody, not even my roommate. Meticulous with my research, I stayed up each evening until six a.m. reading the quatrains and writing them on sheets of computer paper. Once I'd written every quatrain, I began analyzing each, determining that, because the quatrains were written using poetic stanzas, each quatrain could be parsed syllabically. The original quatrains were written in French, and someone thinking logically would assume that the French version would parse differently than the English version; however, I was not thinking logically, assuming that the English version was intended for me and therefore the parsing was correct.

It is common in poetry to follow syllabic patterns. Shakespeare, for example, wrote in Iambic pentameter, meaning there were five feet per line, with a foot consisting of two syllables. It is also common when adhering to poetic forms to follow rhyming patterns. A Shakespearian sonnet, for example, follows the rhyme scheme **abab cdcd efef gg**, with each letter representing a line in the poem and a particular rhyme at the end of the line. Take this (rhymed sections are bolded):

Shall I compare thee to a summer's d**ay**? a
Thou art more lovely and more temper**ate**: b
Rough winds do shake the darling buds of **May**, a
And summer's lease hath all too short a **date**: b


Although Nostradamus's quatrains do not rhyme, some seemed to follow a pattern. For example, here is a syllabic parsing of the following quatrain:

The young lion will overcome the older one, 12
On the field of combat in a single battle; 12

He will pierce his eyes through a golden cage, 10
Two wounds made one, then he dies a cruel death. 10

By counting the syllables in the first line ("the" has one syllable, "young" has one syllable, "lion" has two, etc.), I found that each line usually contains between 8-13 syllables. Most of the quatrains seemed to have completely arbitrary syllabic breakdowns, with the exception of the few quatrains that are suspected to have come true, like the quatrain predicting the French Revolution:

From the enslaved people, songs, chants and demands, 11
The princes and lords are held captive in prisons: 12
In the future by such headless idiots 11
These will be taken as divine utterances. 12

I believed that I had stumbled upon a code for deciphering Nostradamus's other, less famous, quatrains. First I counted all of the syllables of each of his quatrains, and made a list of the numeric representations of each quatrain, the previous being: 11, 12, 11, 12. Then I began the process of rearranging the lines of the less-famous quatrains numerically, so that they more closely followed a poetic system. For instance, if a quatrain had the numeric representation of 9, 8, 9, 13, I searched through the other quatrains, seeking out lines with 8's and swapping them with the 13, then rereading the quatrain and attempting to make sense of it.

Although the lines are extremely vague and are written symbolically (for instance "lions" are used as symbols of real knights like Henry II), the quatrains were beginning to make sense to me. I had read them so many times that ambiguous and symbolic words such as "right" and "reds" that are scattered throughout took on meaning.

I also began to seriously consider the true meaning of the word "time." Because I was superficially familiar with Einstein's Theory of Relativity, I began to see time as something that was not fixed and it became something for which I no longer had a definition. This feeling of being unrooted in time led to feelings of detachment and, eventually, being disconnected from reality.

One evening while opening my mirrored medicine cabinet, which was perpendicular to a large bathroom mirror, I noticed that the two mirrors reflected each other and created a series of mirror images, like silver dominoes descending infinitely into the distance. I stared at this image for a long time and considered it to be a representation of time, as each reflected image represented a microscopic amount of time – the time it takes for light to travel between the two mirrors. Because I viewed the cascading mirror images in a single pane of the looking glass and thus a single image, it was like staring at the past and the present at the same moment. I decided then that time did not exist, because I was witnessing numerous moments as a single moment. Time, from that point on, represented infinity and infinity was for me a single instant without beginning or end.

Deciding that each moment occurred simultaneously, I began to think that each instant was the same instant constantly redefined in the physical world but never actually changing.

I have since decided that the main ingredients for the mad brew I was concocting were infatuation, stress, lack of sleep, drug use, alcohol abuse, and a desire to prove myself. Individually, each of their things is its own debilitating issue, but together they created a high unlike any I had ever known.

There is another, lesser known piece of writing composed by Nostradamus. It was written to his son, Cesar, and seems to describe guidelines for becoming a seer, a sort of prophet. I used this letter as a compass for my studies, believing that it was truly intended for me, whom he referred to as Cesar because of my personal perceived connection with Caesar, the Roman emperor. For the first time in my life, I was beginning to make distorted connections between unlike things, always with myself at the middle; for the first time, I was experiencing delusions of grandeur, a common symptom of manic episodes.

I was encouraged by this line from the letter: "and I do not want to talk of years to come but of the months during which you will struggle to grasp and understand the work I shall be compelled to leave you after my death." Assuming these words were for me, my toils would last only a few months, at which time I would be able to "understand each prophecy in every quatrain herein." Spending many wide-eyed evening and early morning hours contemplating the intent of the letter to Cesar, I became fully convinced that within the letter lay the key to deciphering the quatrains, and I set aside my study of the quatrains and focused on the letter.

Because the letter mentions "that all is ruled and governed by the power of Almighty God, inspiring us not by Bacchic frenzy nor by enchantments but by astronomical assurances" I began to study astronomy, believing it held the keys to prophecy. I spent some evenings on the small porch of my apartment, smelling the dry desert air and listening to the vehicles pass on I-10 while gazing at the stars and formulating a meaning to their existence. It is written in the letter that "the understanding sometimes stirs through contemplation of the distant stars as if in vigil, likewise by means of pronouncements, one finds oneself surprised at producing writings without fear of being stricken for such impudent loquacity. The reason is that all this proceeds from the divine power of Almighty God from whom all bounty proceeds." This statement seemed to vouchsafe my poetry and gave to me a license to write any mad thought that passed through my head.

Life was changing. I began to think of myself as higher than average individuals and believed that my actions were of more import than those of most individuals. Since I had imagined my great significance, every little thing seemed meaningful in some way. I have since learned that feelings of greatness and being "special" are consistent with manic delusions of grandeur, as is not needing sleep.

During this time, I maintained contact with Kate, who seemed to approach my oftentimes incomprehensible emails attempting to describe my findings with calmness and curiosity. I remember one email in which I attempted to decipher certain aspects of prophecy for which, despite my unquestioning obedience during the evening hours, I still had a grain of doubt. I wrote that anything can be predicted so long as you keep the prediction vague, and pointed out that there was a tree outside her window. I didn't actually know whether or not there was a tree, but I felt my vague prediction demonstrated my point. More than once, Kate acted to ground me by pointing out logical flaws in my "theories."

I also wrote to Kate regarding my ideas about time. I wrote, "I am writing this, you are reading this" in one email, demonstrating my belief that time was an illusion and that the time between writing and reading does not exist because the reader perceives both in a single instant. I think Kate was impressed by these concepts and our relationship continued to grow to the point that we were emailing almost daily.

Later in life, Einstein did not believe in the past, present, or future, believing instead that everything happened in a single instant. (I am not comparing myself to Einstein, as he probably reached that conclusion after many hours of reasoned thought, and I reached that conclusion in a flash of madness.) Upon the death of a fellow physicist, he believed that the man's earlier departure was inconsequential, stating, "us physicists believe the separation between past, present, and future is only an illusion, although a convincing one."

I developed a simple equation that I have since lost, and which probably didn't make sense in the first place, because I know next to nothing about formulating equations. The gist of my thoughts were that if time is merely the measure of the expenditure of energy (i.e. it takes energy—that of the battery—to move the hands of a clock), and energy can neither be created nor destroyed, then time is an illusion, because energy is not actually being expended, it is merely changing forms.

Throughout these weeks of research, a conviction that I had some greater role to play in Nostradamus' prophecies and in the future of the planet grew to monstrous proportions. It was my belief that I was well on my way to deciphering Nostradamus's quatrains and therefore on my way to preventing future tragedies. All these thoughts, I am now certain, stemmed from the earlier desire to be more than average. If I could save the world, I would be a great man, perhaps the greatest man to ever live.

I had a sense of responsibility for 9/11 because I felt that A) I could have prevented the tragedy if only I'd read the quatrains earlier and B) that my reading of the quatrains had set into motion the prophecy of the incident. Either way, I had failed and felt responsible for the deaths of countless people.

In my poetry, there was a deepening in religiosity, as notions of infinity led me to again consider the definition of God. I then wrote: God = Infinity.

I also wrote:

They will not always talk,
Poetry is a good start
They'll teach you how to walk
If you respect their art

They'll teach you how to see
How to hear, think, and feel
They'll help to set you free
And raise you above the wheel…

This poem introduces two recurring themes that would amplify during my manic stages, that of "others" speaking to me, in the sense of inspiration and not auditory messages, and that of different levels of existence. Both themes revert back to my favorite work of poetry, Dante's *The Divine Comedy*.

In *The Divine Comedy*, the narrator is guided through hell, purgatory, and paradise, where he finally reaches his goal, reunion with the love of his life, Beatrice, and, ultimately, union with God. Throughout his journey, the narrator is aided by ghosts from the past, such as the poet Virgil and Emperor Justinian. Hell and Heaven are divided into levels, wherein individuals were placed based on their deeds in the material world.

In many ways, *The Divine Comedy* is an allegory about bipolar disorder, with Hell representing depression, purgatory representing a stable, albeit indifferent mood, and paradise representing the euphoria of mania. When I first read *The Divine Comedy* it was from a religious and pious viewpoint, one that I still held at this point in my life, and I truly believed that our actions on earth directly reflected upon our placement in the afterlife, and I believed that I was fated for Heaven.

*The Divine Comedy* is also an allegory for the world as we know it. In the nine circles of Hell, individuals are condemned to fates comparable to their sins, much as individuals today are often condemned by their vices. The greedy, for instance, are condemned to push heavy weights, representing their accumulation of material items. Pimps and seducers are whipped by demons, just as they "whipped" others during their lives.

The letter to Cesar does not mention the circles of Heaven or Hell, but it does say, "In the firmament of the eighth sphere, a dimension whereon Almighty God will complete the revolution, and where the constellations will resume their motion which will render the earth stable and firm, but only if He will remain unchanged for ever until His will be done." One of the outermost spheres in Medieval and Renaissance geocentric astronomy was called the Primum Mobile, or "first moved." The Primum Mobile is the Ninth Sphere in *The Divine Comedy* and is the domain of the angels, as well as the sphere directly moved by God.

At the time, I believed that Nostradamus was referring to this sphere, as I had already read *The Divine Comedy* at this point in my life and felt there was a connection between Nostradamus and Dante. Although their lives were separated by two hundred years, the connection was that they lived in a geocentric universe, one with Earth as its center. My mania was fueled by a seven-hundred-year-old poet and a five-hundred-year-old prophet, and my sources were books dating back to medieval times. As ridiculous as it seems to think about now, I was completely convinced that they spoke the truth, and my universe was quickly becoming their universe.

As I write these words, I realize it has been almost exactly eleven years since these events occurred. My first hospitalization took place in October, 2001. Since then, I have been hospitalized two more times, both in October. I do not like re-reading Nostradamus' quatrains and the *Divine Comedy*, especially in October, because I sense the old thoughts within me, and I have to continually remind myself that these things are not real, that Nostradamus is not speaking to me, that Dante is not laying out the order of heaven for me and inviting me to follow him through the spheres. It is like returning to the location of a traumatic event; you know the event has passed but by revisiting its location your emotions and memories are keener and as real as when it happened. I still recall the daylight creeping around the sides of the venetian blinds of my bedroom in Arizona as I crawled into bed at eight in the morning. I still recall the layout of my desk. I still recall the mad thoughts that seemed so real then, and feel so real when I recall them now.

Throughout this time of growing madness I continued to work as a martial arts instructor and each day, for an hour, I was asked to hand out flyers on street corners, walking into stopped traffic and offering drivers and passengers a black and white flyer with a little kicking karate man on it that provided embellished details of the gym and offered a special sign-up deal. Most people rolled up their windows, afraid or annoyed; others took the flyer out of pity. I learned the trick that all people who hand out flyers must learn: if you hand something to someone, many people will take it. We received five dollars every time a flyer with our initials showed up at the dojo. In my eight months there, I received a total of ten dollars.

My feelings of power and grandeur grew stronger as the mania took hold. Through my constant study of Nostradamus' letter to Cesar, I developed a sense that I was not only his son, but also a saint, and I began viewing those to whom I handed flyers as the "common man," whom I was to look out for. I developed a great sense of oneness with everyone I met, a sort of humility and appreciation for them, and I smiled compassionately at them, thinking each was a child of God. At one point I vividly recall a shirtless, muscular, tattooed Mexican man riding by on a bicycle that was too small for him saying, "Open your heart to Jesus." I took this as a sign, certain that God was communicating to me, and my delusions of grandeur deepened.

I continued my study of time each evening and continued to email Kate on a regular basis, her higher status as an Oxford student giving rise to greater delusions. I thought she was a princess, my Beatrice, who was to guide me to heaven. Trying to find hidden messages that would guide me in my research, I read and reread every email I received from her countless times. Looking back, I think I was in love, which has a madness of its own. To this day, Kate insists that it was not love, only madness. Kate represented my ambitions; she became a symbol of my desires and passions, the focus of my life, the point of my existence. Every thought, no matter how mad, led back to her.

Believing my study of time complete, I decided I would give a speech about it at Oxford.

I called my parents and, without explanation, said I urgently needed to go to Oxford. I would never return to Arizona.

Although at the time I was certain my actions were the actions of a rational mind, my parents understood that something was wrong and immediately agreed to pay for a ticket back to Maryland, insisting I could stay there for a while and fly to Oxford at a later date.

# 4

# The Stars Speak

I remember vividly the flight home. It was early evening and, as I traveled eastward to Maryland, the sky to the east darkened and the sky to the west became red with the sunset. Sitting in the window seat, I constantly looked westward, imagining that a great battle between heaven and hell was occurring, setting fire to the sky, the clouds becoming smoke. I saw or imagined flashes in the sky, the sparks emitted from the clashing swords of angels. Falling, spiraling from the sky, I imagined angels from both sides dying, their purpose fulfilled. Michael led the good angels, Lucifer the bad. So great was this battle that all of the land to the west was caught up in it, but I was not alarmed by this. I simply smiled, feeling the warmth of God upon me, and reassured myself that good would be victorious.

I was rereading *The Inferno* (Book one of *The Divine Comedy*) on the plane. The author of the poem, Dante, spoke directly to me because, as my experiment with time (the "I'm writing this at the same time you are reading it" email to Kate) demonstrated, time did not exist where writing was concerned. Dante spoke to me from the present, from infinite time, and his words were directed at me and intended to bring to light hidden messages within his text that lay dormant for seven hundred years, until I, and only I, was able to read them and hear the words' true meanings. Although many in their early twenties seek purpose, few find that they are the recipients of divine inspiration, and that their purpose extends well beyond this realm into the spheres of heaven. I was happy to have a purpose.

There are lyrics in Bob Dylan's "Tangled up in Blue" that mention a book of poems written by a thirteenth century poet, with words that ring true, glow like burning coals, and are written in the reader's soul.

"Tangled up in Blue" became another signpost that I was chosen and moving in the right direction. Just as in Dylan's song, Dante was an Italian poet in the thirteenth century, and his words certainly rang true for me, as if written from his soul to mine, as though we shared a single soul and a single purpose, his words burning into my head, reaching my deepest subconscious, as hot coals melt through snow.

During each manic episode music played a large role, and songs always spoke directly to me, as they do to many who experience manic episodes. When I hear certain songs today, songs that "spoke" to me during manic episodes, I have to hold back wild thoughts, as though my mind were a horse that was easily spooked, prepared, upon hearing these songs, to take off at a gallop and never look back. I feel the bucking at times, snorting, legs kicking and riling dirt, but, like a seasoned horse rider, I calmly pull back on the reigns and listen to the song for what it is, catching myself before those old haunting thoughts of "maybe I was right, maybe I just didn't go far enough" take hold. It seems to me that sanity is fragile; the sane person walks a very thin line, and one small quixotic thought, whether for love, power, or money, can drive someone into madness for the rest of their life. It is only after having experienced madness that I realize many people live, daily, in controlled delusions about themselves and the people around them and/or obsessions, focusing on a single thing and pursuing it relentlessly – their Beatrice.

At this time I found solace in Pachelbel's "Canon in D Major", which is often played at weddings. The classical Baroque piece never "spoke" to me directly as other songs did, probably because it is an instrumental with no words, and language was so important to me and my particular brand of mania. With ebbing and flowing violins, high-pitched, then low, joyous, then sad, happy, then depressed, "Canon in D Major" has always soothed me and leveled out my mood. It puts to music the bitter sweetness of life. With its ever changing "mood," the song, for me, has come to represent bipolar disorder, and it is a reminder that when there is a period of depression, a period of happiness will eventually follow.

Still obsessed with Nostradamus and having read that Nostradamus foretold the future by looking into fire, after returning to Maryland I spent hours meditating in front of a gas fireplace in my parents' basement, imagining within the flames people, places, and things that had not yet occurred. I never saw actual images in the flames, but within my mind's eye prophecies seemed to unfold in a dim light, the images blurred and always slightly out of my reach. I attributed this to my novice prophetic abilities. If I meditated more, I thought, the prophecies would become clearer.

Having read in Nostradamus' letter the lines: "As regards the occult prophecies one is vouchsafed through the subtle spirit of fire, which the understanding sometimes stirs through contemplation of the distant stars as if in vigil." This statement again confirmed my belief that fire was an important aspect of prophecy. As a direct translation of the words, I began to contemplate the stars the following evening, laying on my back in the grass behind my parents' house and staring for hours at them.

If you stare at a single point for long enough, it starts to move. After a long enough time, the stars began bobbing up and down and, because both *The Divine Comedy* and the movie *It's a Wonderful Life* (a holiday tradition in my family) make reference to angels as stars, I began mapping out the night sky, attributing to each star a dead person's name from history.

I developed a system for determining which star belonged to which soul, basing the brightness of a star on an individual's fame or infamy. My definition of morals and values shifted often during manic episodes and at this particular moment I did not believe in good or evil, seeing the weight of an individual's soul measured only by the effect, whether positive or negative, they had on humanity. These thoughts are deep-seated, and still today I see life in a gray light, feeling at times that the world would be a boring place without bad guys. After all, who wants to see a movie or play about a hero who has no arch nemesis? Good, I have often thought, cannot exist without evil, as the definition of one is relative to the other. One cannot do good if there are no defined rules for what is bad. Once, the result of these thoughts was indifference, which I have long struggled to overcome and, again, detachment from reality. The clinical term for this is apathy, which is another attitude that is strongly associated with bipolar disorder.

As the stars wobbled in the sky, I imagined that they were famous dead people attempting to communicate with me – Aristotle one night, Jesus, Gabriel, or Genghis Khan another. After many evenings of this, I developed a soul rating system based on points.

Being a member of the American society that is often concerned with striving and being the "best," it is only natural that I developed a system for determining the best, most powerful soul. Lives saved and lives taken afforded the same number of points. Extremely evil individuals were given them same amount of points as extremely good ones.

As an explanation of these "gray," ambiguous thoughts – neither black, nor white – I often consider my madness as a deconstruction of my mind, a reversal of all that I had learned as a developing child and adolescent, a dismissal of the most basic human principals. My madness questioned and turned upside down those very basic concepts we learn as babies and toddlers, especially those involving the "great split," the time when our minds split into two parts, when we learn the words "yes" and "no," when everything from that point on is placed into one of the categories of yes and no, good and bad, like and dislike. We are taught right and wrong by our parents, our teachers, in Sunday school, and by internalizing society's laws, but are any actions empirically right and wrong? Was there only "this" and "that" action before we ate the apple and gained the knowledge of good and evil? Are good and evil inherent, or did humans create these concepts? During the mania, these thoughts further unmoored me from society and reality.

Because the North Star is the brightest star and therefore the most powerful, the center star of the entire night sky and the anchor for all others, I honored it with the name "Jesus," whom I considered the most influential soul of all time. This decision was not without debate, as, in Shakespeare's *Julius Caesar,* the title character says, "I am as constant as the Northern Star." I soon determined that Jesus and Caesar were both the North Star, because both were really the same soul, their time on earth separated by a mere 40 years. The names were irrelevant. Although I wrote it at a later time, my play *The Amazing Life of Wilfred Churchill* demonstrates this recurring belief. In it, Jesus and Lucifer play a game of *Yu-Gi-Oh,* a card game played by children, using the souls of famous individuals to determine the course of history for the next 500 years. In previous games, Lucifer and Jesus had played chess, which always ended in a stalemate. In the following excerpt, L is Lucifer and J is Jesus.

## THE AMAZING LIFE OF WILFRED CHURCHILL

Act Two:

L: What's so funny! It's not like you got much use out of

Attila anyway…bringing him back as Jah Rasta. All you did was give stoners a PURPOSE for smoking weed.

L palms one of J's cards when J is not looking.

J: (disregarding L's statement) You wanna trade for…

L: Hmm…(shuffling through his deck) How would you like a perfectly good, reliable…George Bush. (Nodding head) Huh? Yeah?

J: Senior?

L: Looking at card. Nah, W.

J: Hah. Was that the pawn that you tried to queen late in the last game?

L: Yeah.

J: And sacrificed a Knight in the process?

L: Yeah.

J: Even though it was impossible for your pawn to get to the other side of the board without being taken by my queen.

L: (softly) Yeah…You know, I don't criticize your game play.

J: Yes you do!

L: Oh, well do you want the card or not?

J: (thinks for a moment) Who was he last time you played him?

L: It's been a while, at least three games ago…Ah! Nero.

J: (laughing hysterically) I think I'll let you hang on to that one.

L: (groaning and shaking card) I've been trying to get rid of this guy for five millennia. (Throws card on left side of table)

J: And you'll be trying for at least five more. What about this one?

L: Which?

J: Wild Card.

L: Hmm, who was it?

J: Spontaneously combusted at the age of fifteen last time I played 'er, but before that it was Dante.

L: A poet wild card! Are you kidding me? Might as well be trying to sell me the Chernobyl power plant...no thanks. ... ...Actually, lemme see that card. (Takes card and compares it with another). Okay (hands card back), here's what I'll do. Because I'm tired of playing these stupid games, I'm gonna give you an edge this time. What other cards can you offer me, liiiike medium-good cards.

*The Amazing Life of Wilfred Churchill* was written in a period of unsettled sanity between my first and second manic episodes, and it demonstrates that the thoughts, emotions, and ideas experienced during manic episodes never really disappear—they merely lie dormant. Buried beneath mounds of rational thoughts during a period of sanity, these wild ideas are dampened but never quite squelched; they continue to echo from deep within the cave of consciousness, just waiting for the right moment to rear their heads again. However hokey it might be, the play calls to light some of my deep-seated, manic thoughts that, written down during a period of sanity, I employed as a way to look back on the mania with youthful cockiness, mockingly snubbing my nose and believing that unearthing these manic ideas would somehow diminish their power. Mistakenly, I believed that writing the thoughts down, bringing them into the light, would reveal them to be as harmless as other thoughts. In the play, they are harmless, because there is no action tied to them beyond the fake action of the play. However, the danger of mania is that, in real life, these thoughts often *are* tied to action. The words come off of the page and are put into action by the afflicted person. Thus, sprinkled in this play in only a few lines were the seeds of my increasingly political thoughts toward George W. Bush, which would develop into a paranoia that would follow me everywhere I went.

# 5

# The Book of Revelations

As seems the destiny of all people who fall into madness, I began reading the Book of Revelations, keeping the Bible in a nightstand by my bed and staying up all hours of the night attempting to translate its cryptic messages. The days passed quickly and I could no longer discern minutes from hours or days.

I repeatedly read several passages from the Book of Revelations. Firstly, Revelations 1:3 – "Blessed is he that readeth, and they that hear the words of this prophecy, and keep those things which are written therein: for the time is at hand." Secondly:

13 And in the midst of the seven candlesticks one like unto the Son of man, clothed with a garment down to the foot, and girt about the paps with a golden girdle.

14 His head and his hairs were white like wool, as white as snow; and his eyes were as a flame of fire;

I believed that the Book of Revelations was a set of in-
structions, to what I do not know, and I began deciphering
the statements, first believing that the description of the
"Son of man" was actually a symbolic reference to the planet
Earth, with the North Pole as the snowy hair and the Earth's
molten core as the flaming body. I began then thinking that
the body of Christ was simply a way of referencing the
Earth, and that Christ himself was merely a personification
of the planet on which we live.

In Greek myth, anthropomorphic gods often represent
grand objects or ideas. Uranus, for example, represents the
sky and Gaia represents the earth. Although they are clearly
separate things that cannot perform human acts, Uranus and
Gaia reproduce to give birth to the titans, principally Cronus,
who is the father of the Olympian Gods. In Egyptian myth,
Geb is the god of earth, and is also the Earth itself. Because
all myth was at one time religion, it would not be out of the
question for a religion to refer to a god as both human-like
and as the Earth itself. I then read Chapter 12 of the Book of
Revelations, which says:

> 12:3 Another sign was seen in heaven. Behold, a great
> red dragon, having seven heads and ten horns, and on his
> heads seven crowns.
>
> 12:4 His tail drew one third of the stars of the sky, and
> threw them to the earth. The dragon stood before the
> woman who was about to give birth, so that when she
> gave birth he might devour her child.

Attempting to make sense of Revelations, perceiving the dragon to be Satan, I drew a diagram utilizing seven points, as seven is continually referenced throughout the Book. After continuous study and reworking of this diagram, I was faced with the most despairing moment of my life, when I literally felt that the whole world had turned to Hell and I was condemned to live there. I had drawn a pentagram on the paper. I thought this was the key to the Book of Revelations, the revelation being that Satan, represented by the pentagram, is ruling the earth and that we inhabitants are cursed to live our lives in a world full of hate and war: in other words, Hell. I contemplated the rule of Satan, thinking that I may in fact be the antichrist, but I eventually rejected these notions and returned to my studies, drawing on paper a Star of David instead of a pentagram- a much more common-sense conclusion, as the Star of David has six points, with one in the center. I believed that the two equilateral triangles of the Star, one pointing up and the other down, represented the two swords in the Revelations 1:14: "And he had in his right hand seven stars: and out of his mouth went a sharp twoedged sword: and his countenance was as the sun shineth in his strength." The seven stars in the right hand represented the seven points (including the center) of the Star of David.

I took a drive that evening, to where I do not know, but I ended up in the parking lot of a hospital, believing that Christ was soon to be reborn in that very hospital. I waited in the parking lot for a long time, deliberating on my role: was I a Magi, David, or Christ himself? Watching as a car drove slowly by, the driver seeming to take note of my appearance, and now believing that the forces of evil were out to stop me, I drove away from the hospital to a road above it. The road ended in a dark cul-de-sac where there was a house in the process of being constructed. I sat in the dark for some time, trying to think whether I'd like to be Jesus or David. Ultimately, I chose to be David.

However, while driving away I soon adopted the belief that I was Jesus and for some reason I felt that I needed to stay at a stranger's house that evening or Satan would win out—I needed to go back to Jesus' birth in a stranger's manger. I parked my car and approached a house. I can only imagine what I looked like at this time, having not showered or eaten in perhaps days. The house was a two-story in a suburban neighborhood. It was approximately nine o'clock at night when I rang the doorbell.

A man answered and I immediately asked if I could stay at his house that evening, and, flabbergasted, the man said no and closed the door, but continued to watch through a window as I walked to his neighbor's house and rang the doorbell. A Middle Eastern man answered and asked what I wanted; again, I asked if I could stay at his house. More compassionate than the first man, he said no, but wanted to know if something was wrong with me. I said there wasn't and insisted that he let me stay the evening. At this point a small child watched from the stairs, which were back and to the right of the door. The man again refused my request. I began to cry, pleading with him to let me stay, saying, "remember your heritage," thinking that in the past it was inconsiderate to turn away a stranger. At this point the other neighbor came out on his porch and said, "I've called the cops."

Although I was clearly beyond all reason at this moment, mention of the cops immediately sent me to my car, and I drove away thinking the forces of Satan – the cops – were once again after me. I returned home.

Back at my parents' house that evening, I drafted a sort of compendium. First creating a square and dividing it into four parts – Earth, Fire, Wind, Water— I then drew a circle around the square and divided the circle into twelve parts, as a clock is divided. I marked off the seasons and months, added the zodiac signs to their appropriate quadrant, and, on top of that, included a saint in each of the twelve quadrants. I do not remember all of the saints, but I know Moses, Mark, John the Baptist, Mary, and Anne were among them. I also recall assigning animals to certain quadrants, associating Mark with the lion. The point being that this was a very busy piece of paper with a great deal of information crammed into a small space–the perfect representation of a manic mind.

I've tried to recreate the mental processes that led to my beliefs and actions of the time, but have been unsuccessful in developing any coherent method or justification. The best that I can say is that, when experiencing mania, any two thoughts, no matter how distant, can be instantly connected. My mind latched onto ordinary events and attached to them far-out conclusions. The mania seemed to escalate at night and lessen during the day, and I returned to manageable levels the next morning. However, throughout this entire period I continuously mentioned to my family members that I would be giving a speech about time at Oxford, and it was these bizarre comments that led to my mother calling Fr. Jeromy for guidance.

G.H. FRANCIS

Fr. Jeromy was a priest for whom I had done some volunteer work for a Christian service project that was required to graduate from my Catholic high school. In the five years since I had met him he had become a mentor and friend. I had continued volunteering for him after high school, eventually becoming the supervisor of the youth club in which I was formerly a member. The club consisted of four high school boys and four 8- to 12-year-old boys who had been abused or neglected. Designed to provide male role models to the children whose male influences had been anything but role models, we participated in therapeutic activities such as talking sessions during which we sat in a circle and discussed our problems – this was crucial because most of the children had shut out their issues – and we also cooked, played games, and created art together.

Now, convinced I was the son of God, with self-drawn schematics demonstrating the connection between the four elements, the constellations, and the saints, I drove to meet Fr. Jeromy.

After arriving at Fr. Jeromy's place of work, a foster care facility, he immediately ushered me into the library, which consisted of a large oblong table and walls lined with bookshelves. We began speaking and, according to him, I was lucid and completely normal-seeming. For several minutes, we had a fairly common conversation. Then, I told him that I was Jesus. Naturally, he was incredulous and gently attempted to change my thinking. According to Fr. Jeromy, I was incredibly persistent, insisting that Jesus of Nazareth was not the true son of God because he was a carpenter and killed trees, while I was the son of a doctor, a healer, and was the true Jesus. I was aware that he did not believe me and, in a moment that left a great imprint on Fr. Jeromy, I placed both hands on the table, leaned forward, and said while looking him directly in the eyes, "How would you know if the true Jesus really returned?" I thought that if the true Jesus did return he would receive the same reaction I was receiving, and he'd end up in a mental hospital unless he was able to perform miracles.

For both Father Jeromy and me this also called into question the validity of Jesus of Nazareth, who, rather than being the Son of God, could very easily have experienced a similar untreated mania, and in this mania performed actions to fulfill this delusion, such as riding a donkey into Jerusalem (commemorated on Palm Sunday), which is considered the fulfillment of the following prophecy in Zechariah:

See, your king comes to you,
righteous and having salvation,
gentle and riding on a donkey, on a colt, the foal of a
    donkey.

Having known the existence of this prophecy, could Jesus not have performed this action in order to fulfill his own delusion? This, again, tugs at the root of faith, because true Christians must have faith that this was not the case.

No longer interested in conversation, I asked Father Jeromy if there was a Bible in the room, and he removed one from the bookshelves. Starting at Genesis 1: "In the beginning God created the heavens and the earth," I began reading with the intention of reciting the entire Book.

At this time, Fr. Jeromy got up to call the police, and I followed him through the foster center to the phone, continually reading the Bible as I did so, believing that the Bible would have the same effect on him that it had on me: it would speak to him and prove that I was the Son of God. He contacted my parents and the police.

My parents arrived first, followed shortly afterwards by the police and paramedics. I continued reading as the police and paramedics gathered in the lobby of the center, and I was fully compliant with the paramedics, willingly walking to the ambulance. I began crying. This, according to Fr. Jeromy, "broke his heart." As the ambulance door was about to be closed I looked out to Father Jeromy and said I wasn't crying for me, I was crying for him because he didn't believe me.

# 6

# Institutionalization

A s I write these words, it's been approximately eleven years since the ambulance doors closed. I remember very little of the trip. I had closed my eyes, thinking all light to be the brilliance of God and, as I was wheeled into the hospital (a regular hospital, not a mental hospital), a man spoke comforting words to me. My eyes still closed, I heard a certain bass in his voice and asked if he was black. He said yes. And I told him that his people had suffered more than any other and would be rewarded by God. I do not recall his response.

I was taken into a small, dimly lit room and placed on a hospital bed. The light being less bright, I opened my eyes in time to see three nurses holding me down and sticking a large needle into my butt. As I wandered into sleep, I looked at my mother, who was the only remaining person in the room, and her face seemed mad and evil, as though she enjoyed the torment I was receiving, and my last thoughts were that she may have been a demon.

When I awoke I was on another gurney in an unknown hallway and a paramedic was speaking with a woman behind a sliding glass window, like the ones at doctor's offices. I was very groggy, but I remember this vividly. I was wheeled down corridors and remember watching lights pass above me, like those shots in movies and hospital dramas seen from a patient's perspective, with the long rectangular lights going by like center lines on a highway. Soon, I was wheeled past two steel doors and was again waiting in front of a window, which turned out to be the nurse's station of Ward A-1 at the Shepherd Pratt hospital, a well-known psychiatric hospital located just north of Baltimore. I fell asleep.

When I awoke I was in a room that was approximately 12 ft. by 12 ft., and I was still in my clothes. I knew I had been checked into a mental hospital. If I recall correctly, the door was unlocked and I walked into the main corridor. It was approximately eleven o'clock at night. I stood across from a large room with many chairs and a table near the window on the other side. To my left was a long corridor, to my right were the double white metal doors, locked at all times so patients could not leave, and the nurse's station, which always had a light on. I do not recall by who or how I was oriented to my new environment – I was still very groggy.

The following morning, still very confused, I ate my breakfast with the rest of the patients at two long tables in the common room. I don't recall what I ate but, based on other breakfasts eaten there, I can say with confidence that the food was most likely oatmeal, a small bowl of canned sliced peaches or some such fruit, toast, and coffee that was so watered down it wouldn't wake up a drowsy baby. One of the patients, a tall, emaciated-looking man with white hair, a sallow face, and large glasses, boasted that he was related to Herman Munster, and was quite adamant when anybody denied this claim.

After breakfast I was seated in a room with a doctor and one other person. The room was cool and smelled of the steel table in the center and the tiles on the floor. The doctor asked me a series of questions – the exact questions I do not recall – and then held up a pencil vertically, asking me to follow it with my eyes. I did. He seemed satisfied. Later I learned that this technique is used to determine if a patient has schizophrenia, as schizophrenics often have difficulty following things with their eyes. I was very angry when I realized this, and wrote the following passage in my second book, *Lightbearer*, which was intended to be a retelling of the events you are now reading but instead developed into a mad, drunken mess:

> He slowly moved the pencil, first horizontally and then vertically, as in a priestly blessing. The beady-eyed, big-headed psycho-mind-fucking bastard thought I was schizophrenic – I should have bit the pencil in half and poked his little eye out with the pointy end. Then, with graphite and yellow pencil splinters mewling from my mouth, I should have jumped on the table and blathered like an idiot.
>
> I wasn't schizophrenic.

The reference to "his little eye" reflects a delusion that would later occur during my second manic episode regarding the Illuminati, the suspected society behind the one-eyed pyramid on the one dollar bill.

I would further write of this meeting:

He sat for a moment staring out from behind his glasses and his round face beneath his wide forehead and thinning brown hair. He pressed his long index fingers together and brought them to his thin lips, then he said, "I believe you are bipolar."

There was no long pause for consideration or great moment of acceptance, or any sort of alleviation. I just felt numb.

From that point on, I was trained in dealing with my disease and was asked to accept my new identity as a victim of mental illness. In some ways I was relieved, as I'd long hoped to be unique. They gave me pamphlets, brochures, and books explaining my diagnosis, but these documents do not capture the feeling of the illness, merely the effects of it.

They started me on medications; I don't remember which ones, but I suspect that valporic acid (the brand name is Depakote) was included; I would be on it for 7 years. The medications made me so tired that I rarely thought delusional things — I could barely think at all. I was moved the following day to a different room, a long room with three beds, which were more like cots, and two windows – one window overlooking the grassy courtyard in the center of the building, the other overlooking a parking lot. I spent most of the day sleeping and wallowing in depression.

Staff entered and exited my room throughout the day, asking if I was interested in participating in activities. I always said "no." Note: if you're ever in a mental institution, always do the activities or they will keep you there indefinitely, as I was to learn later during my second hospitalization.

I had two roommates. One I do not remember, the other was a tall, blond-haired man—whose hair reminded me of Harry Dunn's in the film, *Dumb and Dumber*— in his forties, an alcoholic who walked around all day with black 80s-style sunglasses, trudging along as if his feet could not leave the ground, drawn downward by the Earth's gravitational pull so his only mode of conveyance was to exhaustingly drag them across the smooth tile floor of the hallway or thin carpet of the common room. I don't recall having spoken to him; I rarely spoke to anyone. I was in my own world, attempting, once the effects of the medicine wore off, to piece together the past few months, attempting to cope with my new illness, attempting to figure out who I was.

I had been many things in the past few months – a saint, David, Lucifer, Jesus – and I no longer had a feeling of self. My personality, if ever I had one, no longer existed. Struggling with this loss of self today, I still question my identity in groups of people. I catch myself mimicking the lingo of the group (which my therapist tells me is a common, normal practice) and, realizing that I have co-opted their language and thinking that perhaps I have adopted their identity and am offending them, I sit quietly for the rest of the evening feeling that I have no role or personality; I am a leech, I am faceless, I do not exist. Because of my lack of a confident identity, I do not like social settings; they make me uncomfortable.

In The Doors' song "The End", Jim Morrison talks about a killer taking a face from "the ancient gallery."

Although my obsession with Jim Morrison would not occur until my second and third major manic episodes, these words resonate with me: "the ancient gallery of faces," the place where you can take on any face and personality.

The most accurate representation of a mental hospital that I have ever seen is in *One Flew over the Cuckoo's Nest*. The nurses really call "medication time" and, by some coincidence, in my case the residents actually took votes on who wanted to watch the baseball game. The game always lost out to the nightly movie, and anyone interested in watching the game, generally a single African-American man, was forced to watch it in a back room, a sort of semi-circle sitting room with stained glass windows and a small television. Once, I sat with him for a few minutes, but I didn't care about the game.

There are daily activities such as board games and beach ball volleyball, which I also wrote about in *Lightbearer*:

They were playing chair volleyball, perhaps one of the most pathetically entertaining sports on the planet. This is how it is played: a small volleyball net is erected in the common area splitting it in two. Chairs are then placed in two rows of three on either side of the net. Those patients who've opted to play the game sit in the chairs and a large beach ball is thrown into the air and the game begins! You're not allowed to leave your chair; however, one finds constant joy in watching patients overextend themselves then fall, arms reaching with closed fists, to the floor. No score is tallied.

The depressed patients strike the ball in an amusingly lackadaisical manner, their wrists limply backhanding the air as though swatting flies from their faces on a porch in the summertime. The over-stimulated patients grin and watch the ball with hypnotic focus, their eyes tiny planets awaiting orders from some greater being.

*Lightbearer* is a sort of synthesis of experiences from my first two hospitalizations, and I refer to it now because my feelings about these incidents were then fresh. Of psychiatric wards, I would write:

> Psychiatric wards are surreal. The mentally wounded shuffle around all day in their slippers, unshaved and unkempt, with dead faces that stare ahead of, yet see only behind, their inverted gazes. The well-medicated patients smile in a smirking manner befitting mannequins and porcelain dolls. Everybody and everything takes on the characteristics of a cartoon.

The tone of *Lightbearer* is sarcastic and irreverent because, during my alcoholic binges while writing the novel, and on a long search for myself, I believed I was a tough cynic. The title for *Lightbearer* comes from a title attributed to Lucifer (a.k.a. Satan). The name Lucifer is taken from the Latin *lucem ferre,* which is translated as "light bearer." Lucifer is also the name of a star in the sky, often referred to as the morning star, which is actually the planet Venus. At the point of naming the book, I believed Lucifer was actually the most loyal of angels, whose job it was to punish the wicked, assigned to do so by God. I also liked the contrast of Satan, the darkest of angels, being referred to by his other name, light bearer, which meant the exact opposite. This name, to me, was the embodiment of bipolar—the darkness of depression and the light of mania.

On the second evening of my hospitalization, a screaming woman was wheeled into the ward on a gurney. I remember she had long, curly black hair, was fairly attractive, and was in her mid-twenties. She was wheeled to the holding room that I was originally in and several nurses followed, most likely giving her a dose of the ol' butt needle because she calmed down after that. The following day she was very sedate, but in the evening she began talking about her baby, saying "my baby is alright," and such things, and she wrote on the dry erase board in the front of the room — the board used to write down tips on managing our illnesses or coping with drug addictions — a series of numbers, which seemed to make a great deal of sense to her but were complete nonsense to the rest of us. While doing this she continued to speak about her baby. Later in the evening, as a nurse was leaving the ward through the steel doors, she attempted to escape but was caught halfway through the door and dragged kicking and screaming back into the ward. The following day she was gone. I have often wondered if her baby had died, if that's why she was insane.

In mental hospitals, patients are generally either very loud or very quiet. You remember the loud ones, but the quiet ones fade into the background, meekly eating their meals and sitting in corners like frightened children for most of the day. I was a very quiet patient, and I don't recall talking to anyone other than doctors or nurses. I felt like a shadow on an overcast day, when shadows are barely perceptible because the light only trickles through the clouds. I felt like the real me was lost in the madness, and what was left was just flesh, bone, and a numb mind that couldn't make decisions, couldn't think sane thoughts, and couldn't function in the real world.

In many ways, mental hospitals are the worst place to be when you are sick. In them, you are surrounded by other sick people whose mad thoughts can only enflame your own, and whose depression surrounds you like vines on a decaying tree trunk. Mental hospitals may lead to depression and, in the worst case, institutionalization, as was the case with my second hospitalization.

One day I was taken to what appeared to be an examination room, such as the ones you find in doctor's offices, with a chair in the middle, like the chairs at dentist's offices. I was asked to sit in the chair. I did. A woman explained that she was going to take some readings and then she began spreading a gel on little electrodes and placing them on my head, parting my hair so the electrodes connected with the skin of my scalp. The electrodes were attached to wires; I must have looked like some sort of robot. I later learned that this was called an EEG, or Electroencephalogram, which was most likely used to check whether all my neurons were firing properly or if I had severe brain problems.

Soon after that I was discharged, with orders to return each day for two weeks to their outpatient program. The program went on for several hours a day and we—the instructors and patients—spent the time going over handouts and watching videos. The only video I remember was called *Dark Glasses and Kaleidoscopes – Living with Manic Depression*. The instructor kept saying to me, "this one is for you." All I recall from that period was the dull gray air of fall. Later I wrote a flash story that would describe my feelings at the time:

## THE GOLDFISH

The oak shivers in the autumn wind – it is nearly December – the air is metal, scratched by the tree's clawing, naked branches. The knobby, crooked lines of the trees cast no shadows – the sun is gone.

The candle flame wearily dances within its circular prison, glaring curiously at the darkened world, raging at the darkened world. Oh, to leap free, to touch the scattered leaflets and enflame the solemn table, the cold house, the empty world. The goldfish swims in its fishbowl, wavering, drinking its water and slowly dying.

Piano notes flutter through the air, rising and dropping with the currents, wrapping around each other, dancing through the scarred metal.

She touches the frozen windowpane. Heat vents out from beneath her tender palm and scatters a moist, hand-shaped print across the glass. The print lingers and then disappears. She stares through the world.

Her eyes see the commerce of a thousand cities. An Indian man works his loom on the cracked and narrow streets of an unknown city. Her hand, pressed against the smooth glass, feels the soft thread as it passes delicately through his hand. He completes a modest tapestry. He folds the tapestry, places it aside, and begins working on a new one.

A young American, somewhere in a big city, pumps his arm in celebration. His proposal was accepted – "India, woooo!"

The goldfish, gulping its last breaths, stares out from its cylindrical prison, thinking: "Oh, to leap free, to touch the scattered leaflets and enflame the solemn table, the cold house, the empty world."

That is how it is. You feel trapped, like a goldfish in a bowl looking out at the world but always confined within your glass enclosure, numb to everything, imagining the world going on without you, wishing to break free but watching the water around you slowly evaporate. The recurring theme of anti-capitalism occurs in this story; capitalism is portrayed by the young American. I had also read the autobiography of and been influenced by Gandhi, hence the Indian man working on a loom (Gandhi worked on a loom every day). Gandhi once said, "A man is but the product of his thoughts. What he thinks, he becomes." This statement rings true for me, because, in a time when I did not know who I was, I was thinking and becoming many different things.

The medication makes you so numb that you feel like the gray sky— lifeless, colorless, and emotionless. This is the depression. Your mind and body feel like lead. Weak and malleable, strips of you are shorn off by the wear and tear of everyday life, until you feel nothing of you remains; you are merely a moving vessel of flesh and bone.

Around this time I wrote:

## TINY PRIMATE VESSELS

Come with me on a journey through
the seas of destiny.
Sky and ocean, both endless blue
call out for discov'ry.
Sail we each from different ports
and harbors we call home.
Led by drifters and lost escorts,
in waters all alone.
Looking forward to tomorrow,
forgetting of the past.
The ocean our tears of sorrow,
and rain the tears we laugh.
The sun be hope and always east,
the moon is love indeed.
Come the swelt'ring summer heat,
it's winter that we grieve.
Destiny sways and always flows
her waves this ship have shook.
Our weathered souls can never know
the next page of this book.

The title reflects my belief at the time that we are all simply "primate vessels," merely souls inhabiting rudimentary, primitive bodies. I believed that life was a game, that our souls merely played with the bodies we inhabited, and the bodies were not actually us, just some rough translation of who we really are. This belief echoed my extreme feelings of detachment and lack of identity. I thought I had suffered the worst of it, but destiny had a different path for me.

7

# A Ladder of Angels

Secretly conducting nightly meditations, writing poetry, and still studying the concept of time each evening. Months passed and I began serving tables at Carrabba's, a chain Italian food restaurant where I had worked prior to leaving for Arizona. Although I seemed to function normally to others, still as quiet as I had always been, internally I was struggling with a returning madness, which at the time seemed completely rational. Taking my medication only intermittently, I felt that my thoughts led to the way out of this world, a world which was merely a play, a puppet show conducted by great souls – the stars – with lesser souls becoming the unwilling participants. To me, everyone else was mad, a lost cow in the herd.

Believing the battle between good and evil to be real and quite tangible on this planet, and the "grayness" of morality only relevant beyond this sphere of existence, I believed that I could see the "true" angelic or demonic faces of my customers.

By looking into their eyes, I could see good or evil. The reflection of light in "good" eyes was brighter, and I imagined this reflection to be a microcosm of their star. Evil eyes contained no light, with the surrounding face distorted, crooked and vile. Children were always good and innocent of the battle. How I functioned at this time I do not know, because I had slipped entirely into madness and would not recover for at least a month. So begins the second stage of my first manic episode.

Each evening I watched a reality television show called *Crossing Over*, which featured John Edward, a psychic apparently capable of communicating with the audience's dead family members. I watched this show religiously, two episodes a night, starting at 11 p.m. Because of Edwards' inexplicable ability to speak with the dead, I assumed he was a reincarnated John the Baptist, given the same first name as he had held in a previous life.

Attempting to connect my soul with the highest sphere in heaven, I began thinking of the deceased people with whom I held a connection, again reverting back to *The Divine Comedy*, thinking of each departed person as a soul to guide me through Paradisio, each a rung on a ladder who would help me connect to the next level, or sphere. In medieval thought there was something known as the "angelic hierarchy," which attributes certain angels to certain spheres of heaven. The most common angels are simply called "angels" and are what we commonly associate with that name. Less common angels include Archangels, Seraphim, and Cheribum, which, during this manic episode, I inaccurately associated with *putti*, angels in the form of infants. Mixing and matching information in a manner that suited my needs and injecting my own beliefs into this system, I made a direct line to God through the ladder of souls with whom I had a connection, however dim.

My first connection was through J., a young man who had committed suicide, an act resulting, or so I determined, in banishment to hell because suicide was a sin. J. had been sexually abused when he was a boy by a camp counselor, whom he and his family had grown to trust. Believing it to be a safe environment, J. was allowed to stay at the camp counselor's house one summer evening. The counselor took pictures of the abuse.

J. was a painter and his artwork is featured at St. Vincent's Center in Timonium, MD and is often used by Fr. Jeromy to teach law enforcement officers about sexual abuse. Of all the souls in my "chain," he was the most important because he could lift me out of hell into the hands of the angelic souls with whom I had a connection. He protected me from all other evil souls, holding back the pedophiles, things I considered equal if not worse than murderers, the demons that would attempt to hold me in hell, groping my legs and seducing me with false promises. He connected me; he saved me. Without that connection I would have never been able to leave my metaphysical hell, and who knows what would have happened then.

My next connection in the angelic hierarchy was the identical twin of my brother's girlfriend (now my sister-in-law), who had died while a sophomore in college two years prior to this incident. Because she had a living identical twin, this relationship served as a connection between the physical world and the spiritual world, directly connecting me with heaven and linking me with the spheres.

My grandfather, who died only a few months before my birth, was the next link in the angelic chain. Although I never met him, I've always felt as though he was looking out for me, and many members of my family feel that we are similar in appearance. These thoughts of my grandfather looking out for me were magnified tenfold during this manic episode, and I could practically feel his presence.

The final link in the angelic hierarchy, the one that would take me to God, was my younger sibling who was miscarried. Being unborn, this sibling was as innocent as a soul could possibly be, and was therefore closest to God. Having a direct line to God, I wondered who I truly was, again believing that souls returned to earth under different names but with the same temperament.

Despite staring into the fire for long periods of time, imagining faces and listening for voices, I was unable to commune directly with the dead, so I decided I would visit the television psychic, John Edward. After some Internet research, I learned that he was speaking in Wichita, Kansas in a few days. I printed the directions and prepared for my drive. At this point, I was so deep in my madness that I have no idea how my behavior slipped under people's radars, and it is a wonder that I was not hospitalized at that time. It goes to show that despite a person's outward appearance you never have a clue what's actually going on in their mind.

Around this time I completed my manuscript, *Running East*. Initially an anti-capitalist statement, the story's meaning changed several times throughout its writing and in the years to come, and there has never been a coherent ending, just tentative finishes piled up on top of one another. I remember crying every time I wrote an ending. When you spend so much time on a book you develop a bond with the characters, and the ending signifies having to say goodbye to them, having to let them go.

Here are a few endings, all of which take place after the death of the character named Freeman:

Soco's friendship with Freeman seemed so distant and dream-like. Since the funeral, Freeman's words became ethereal and echoed only in the remoteness of Soco's waning memories, which had already begun to be replaced by fantasies of how events may have happened. Although Soco thought often of their experiences, the reality of their friendship had died with Freeman. The gaps were filled with nostalgia, the bad times filled by good.

Soco gazed down the corridor of memories that he had shared with Freeman. He looked out the window at the multitudes of passing pedestrians: some were tall, some short; some old, some young; some happy, most sad. A gust of wind blew open the front door of the diner, bringing with it a swirl of autumn leaves. Soco leaned over and picked up a maple leaf. Its colors reminded Soco of a frozen sunset.

"The leaves," Soco said as he twirled the leaf's stem between his index finger and his thumb, "they've finally changed."

"Can't be green forever," Jakob said as he shook his head and shrugged.

"Yeah, I guess not," Soco stared whimsically out the window and smiled.

The metaphor of change appeared throughout the book, usually referring to the humdrum life of Soco Killman (because the name means, "Society Kills Man") and his eventual realization that he must make his life become something new, something better. Like Soco and many individuals on this planet, I was seeking some sort of change, some awe-inspiring moment that would wake me up and show me the "real world." What I've learned in life is that these moments of external inspiration are few and far between; if you want change you have to make it yourself.

And another ending:

Soco's legs glided swiftly across the slender blades of grass and his arms beat rhythmically, acting as billows for the clean autumn air. Soco remembered the thoughts that used to fly through his head when he ran as a younger man – when you're getting tired and can't run another step, run faster.

He still had endurance, and arrived at work only a few minutes late. Soco didn't have any difficulty fabricating a lie for his boss, he did, however, find it difficult to explain his missing shoes. He said in his mind, "you have the endurance and strength; now you have the will."

The original ending, written in Australia during my solo, has an elderly Soco walking with a cane through a field, hearing and watching the wind brush the long blades of grass, the wind covering any trace of his path. He collapses and smells the fresh earth before he dies.

The multiple endings represent my confusion with life at the time and throughout the years to follow, a confusion shared by many twenty-one-year-olds. I was convinced I should "run east" towards the rising sun, towards new things and a different life, but I wasn't sure which direction "east" was. The initial idea was that east was the direction away from capitalism and the 9-5 work week, away from normalcy and repetition, away from what I considered mundane servitude. However, in later versions of the story, written, I think, after I had realized the great difficulties that lie in turning away from society's rituals and the naiveté of thinking that I was special, I had Soco return to work. The change of Soco returning to work, instead of running off into the sunrise, came because I had initially written the book with the notion of freeing the common man, but, realizing that it was unrealistic and arrogant to free all men from their lives, I decided I would let them know that a 9-5 was okay, that their lives were not pointless, and that true freedom lies in how they thought about the world and not in the jobs they held.

I would later write:

## HOW WE RAN

How we ran
Without direction
We saw the darkness
And how we ran away

Oh how we tired
The darkness seemed to grow
And we'd no place left
Nowhere else to go
Nowhere else to go

Except toward dawn

CHAPTER

# 8

# The Psychic

John Edward's public reading was in Wichita, Kansas in two days. The distance from my parents' house in Timonium, MD to the Cotillion Ballroom in Witchita, Kansas was exactly 1,267 miles. According to Google maps, the drive should take 20 hours and 53 minutes. Alerting only my parents that I would be leaving, I left at about 10 am the following morning, traveling along I-70 through the mountains of Western Maryland, south of Pittsburg, through Columbus and Dayton, Ohio, to Indianapolis, Indiana, all the while thinking I was soon to be reunited with John the Baptist. Again warping and manipulating my delusions until they fit into the empty spaces of the puzzle I believed I was assembling, I decided that his ability to speak to spirits was a way of "baptizing" them for heaven, cleansing their troubled souls of their baggage before sending them to the afterlife.

A twelve-hour drive was the last thing I needed at the time, because the long stretch of my own ruminating thoughts only deepened the madness. Without any need to keep it together or talk with others, I was losing my sense of self, and without that tether there is almost always a wild flight into mania, or a violent fall into depression.

What is referred to as a "cold and hot reader," John Edward's so-called "psychic" abilities can be attributed to fast talking and quick thinking. According to The Skeptic's Dictionary (www.skepdic.com):

> *Cold reading* refers to a set of techniques used by professional manipulators to get a subject to behave in a certain way or to think that the cold reader has some sort of special ability that allows him to "mysteriously" know things about the subject. Cold reading goes beyond the usual tools of manipulation: suggestion and flattery. In cold reading, salespersons, hypnotists, advertising pros, faith healers, con men, and some therapists bank on their subject's inclination to find more meaning in a situation than there actually is. The desire to make sense out of experience can lead us to many wonderful discoveries...

There are numerous techniques used in cold reading, including "fishing"—utilizing common objects to draw a reaction from a victim—and vague statements, such as, "I sense you've lost someone close to you." Various resources claiming that John Edward is a fraud have noted that, while sitting in the audience of *Crossing Over,* they witnessed countless stabs in the dark by the "psychic" and, according to one source, he once made up to forty queries before receiving a positive response from the audience. However, thanks to clever editing, the show depicts John Edward as a phenom capable of accurately describing things and events he could not possibly know, and watching the show one can't help but think his ability is genuine. Others have claimed that the *Crossing Over* staff planted bugs throughout the venue and listened as audience members waited in line for the show – often for many hours – and divulged information regarding lost loved ones. Utilizing a technique known as hot reading, in which the "psychic" uses already-known information to make a reading, as would be the case if he studied the tapes from the bugs, John Edward often, according to one source, appeared to search the audience for faces he recognized, zeroing in on these predetermined unsuspecting victims with specific information about their dead ones.

I have, in the time since my manic episodes, become a great skeptic, distrusting anything that is not directly confirmed by proof that I personally can observe. Perhaps this is a repercussion of my thoughts and actions, a way of preventing them from ever happening again by disbelieving every mystical concept, and, by doing so, protecting myself from another episode of madness.

I have often wondered about the morality of such "psychic" practices, assuming they are fake. On one hand, there is manipulation of people's hopes and dreams and the exploitation of their loved ones for the "psychic's" gain. On the other hand, the readings help assuage many believers' fears, and gives them one final opportunity to speak with a loved one, perhaps giving them a sense of closure they would not otherwise have been able to obtain. This argument leads to questions regarding the validity of heaven, and whether, even if it is known not to exist, it is morally wrong to have people believe it does.

In the movie *The Invention of Lying* the main character exists in a world without lies, where, given any question, the inhabitants will respond absolutely honestly. If, for instance, a wife asked her husband, "Does this dress make me look fat," the husband may respond, "Yes, your spare tires are clearly pressed up against its sides, making you look especially overweight, but I don't think any dress can help that, you're just fat." The main character of the movie learns that he has the ability to lie, something no other person has ever had the ability to do, and any lie he tells will be believed without question, such as the lie he tells a beautiful woman: "The world will end if we don't have sex together." Getting to the point, as his mother is dying she begins crying and tells him she is afraid. So, he tells her there is a place you go when you die, the greatest place you can imagine, where everyone gets mansions and everything they ever dreamed of. Comforted, his mother dies happy and unafraid. Word spreads about this magical afterlife until the entire world awaits his description of the place he refers to as "heaven." Answering their questions as best he can, the main character explains that you only go to this place if you do good things, and bad people are not welcome there. As a result, people intend to do good things in their lives. The point is this: whether or not heaven exists is irrelevant; if it makes people feel good and do good things, it is a good thing. Right?

However, what if someone believes in heaven so much they are willing to drive 1,267 miles to see a "psychic" whom they think is John the Baptist and has the keys to the afterlife? What if someone believes in heaven so much they imagine an Irish girl they met in New Orleans to be Beatrice from *The Divine Comedy* guiding them through the celestial spheres to be seated at the right hand of God?

I pulled over at some point to call Carraba's because I was supposed to be working that evening. It was nighttime and, in the pre-cell phone era, I called from a payphone, speaking to Meg, a woman whose age was disputable because she had graying hair but a young face, yet seemed wise for whatever age she was, and I told her that I was traveling to Kansas "to help an old friend." By old friend I meant God, but even in my delirium I seemed to know that such a statement would make me seem mad. Exasperated, she went in search of the proprietor of Carraba's, who took his time getting to the phone and was extremely annoyed when speaking with me. He told me if I did not come to work that night, I would not have a job. Having a greater purpose, this did not faze me in the least.

After over 600 miles of driving, I stopped at a Knights Inn. I do not know exactly where I was (I don't think I even knew at the time) but my best guess is that I was in the outskirts of Indianapolis, just as I-70 connects with 465—the beltway. The hotel was on one of those access roads you see next to interstates, with a few gas stations, fast food joints, hotels, and restaurants filled with passersby who stop to fill up their vehicles or grab a bite to eat before forgetting they were ever there, clumping the experience with every other exit ramp they've ever gotten off on. I can't say that I remember anything about that night except that I stayed in a Knights Inn, and I found significance in the name. I recall pondering King Arthur and the Knights of the Round Table, imagining Arthur to be one of the lights in heaven, a great soul whose knights surrounded him at a great celestial table. I often associated the 12 Knights of the Round Table with the 12 hours on a clock, the 12 seasons of the months, the 12 astrological signs, the 12 tribes of Israel, and the 12 saints, apostles, and prophets I chose to complete the compendium I carried with me the night I was first taken to a mental hospital.

The following morning I awoke around 8 a.m. and ate breakfast at a Waffle House, sitting at the counter and ordering waffles, speaking to no one, and believing once more that I was a humble saint. My waitress was a woman in her forties—tall with a short haircut that seemed years out of style. Whether she saw the aloofness in my eyes or was just busy I cannot say, but she left me to myself. At the end of the meal I slipped a fifty dollar bill under my empty plate as a tip for my eight dollar meal. My extravagant tip was another sign of my precarious mental health—lavish spending sprees are a common symptom of bipolar mania. It is not uncommon for those experiencing a manic episode to spend well beyond their means or even go deeply into debt due to reckless spending sprees. Other reckless behaviors include sexual promiscuity, abuse of drugs and alcohol, and poor business decisions.

I began the final 600 mile stretch to Wichita, Kansas, where my destination was the Cotillion Ballroom, a medium-sized venue that hosted entertainers, bands, and, apparently, psychics. I do not remember much of the drive. I know I listened to rock music, occasionally playing a mix CD that featured songs such as The Eagles' "Take it Easy", Creedence Clearwater Revival's "Fortunate Son", and Bob

Dylan's "Hurricane". I know I didn't stop for lunch, snacking instead on Snickers bars and beef jerky, and in my manic state I didn't once feel tired.

I have no idea how many cups of coffee one would have to drink in order to feel the alertness associated with mania—five maybe. However, as happens when you drink large quantities of coffee, along with the alertness you experience extreme anxiety, your heart racing for hours on end, and you feel that dropping sensation in your chest, the one you get when plummeting toward earth on a rollercoaster.

To those who have not experienced it, mania is a difficult thing to describe. The mind is like a river during a torrential downpour, swelling beyond its banks, the current moving so swiftly that objects rush in and out of view in mere seconds. The objects in the river: a tire, a refrigerator, a car (for example) are completely arbitrary; however, in mania (in my mania anyway) all objects are somehow connected to each other. It is as if you are experiencing one constant thought—the river—and every notion that crosses your mind—the objects in the river—adds to that thought, so that at some point in the river the objects bottleneck and form a dam, representing the "completed" thought, which makes absolutely no sense whatsoever to anyone but the person in whose mind it occurs. Sample scenario: The tire represents the moon, because it is round and black; the refrigerator represents the sun, because it has a light inside it; and the car represents Cerberus, the three headed dog of the underworld, because it has four "legs" (wheels) and you must travel to the underworld in order to free the moon and the sun. Whatever the object that floats down the river, you will make it part of your narrative, because if it is in the river it must have significance. Everything happens for a reason.

Everything happens for a reason: the single most destructive thought that has ever entered my mind. Saying that to a manic or a schizophrenic is like lighting a match and handing it to a pyromaniac with a stick of dynamite. This seemingly innocuous statement, often used to explain coincidences or console people during difficult times, gives meaning to random occurrences, links opposites, and proliferates thoughts that a higher (or lower) being is in control, pulling the strings, using your body as a conduit for its most trivial whims. When taken to an extreme, "everything happens for a reason" is a recipe for madness, the key ingredient in a poison so potent it can turn an average twenty-one-year-old into a raving lunatic.

According to www.psychcentral.com:

A manic episode is a discrete period (at least 1 week) of persistently elevated, euphoric, irritable, or expansive mood. Symptoms may include hyperactivity, grandiosity, flight of ideas, talkativeness, a decreased need for sleep, and distractibility. Manic episodes, often having a rapid onset and symptom progression over a few days, generally impair occupational or social functioning, and may require hospitalization to prevent harm to self or others. In an extreme form, people with mania frequently have psychotic hallucinations or delusions. This form of mania may be difficult to differentiate from schizophrenia or stimulant intoxication.

*Copyright 2015 Psych Central.com. All rights reserved. Reprinted here with permission.*

The order of events in Wichita is a bit hazy. I remember being outside the main city, where old strip malls, car dealerships, and liquor stores were stretched out along a single main road, Route 54, the area seeming to reject innovation and change, the residents stuck in the old way of building and conducting business. I checked into a cheap hotel near the Cotillion Ballroom—I don't remember which one. These specific memories are lost to me, unlike most memories from my manic episodes, which are so vivid that I often wish I could forget them as well, the shame and pain of them causing me a great deal of internal embarrassment.

CHAPTER

# 9

# The Cotillion Ballroom

The Cotillion Ballroom looks like a 1950's-era UFO nestled into a parking lot, the building circular with a domed center and a large ring along the exterior, like a donut with a hump where the hole should be. In front of the entrance, four tall poles are topped with red or blue spheres, adding splendidly to its otherworldliness. The exterior of the building is robin's egg blue while the roof is white with a yellow or gold button at the top of the dome. From above, the building probably looks like the breast of a giant porcelain goddess.

I purchased my ticket for fifty dollars and, after scanning the rows of chairs for a place to sit, set up camp in an old phone booth at the back of the ballroom. I sat on the small wooden seat and was asked by kind-hearted individuals several times during the show if I'd like to come out. I responded "no" to each request.

The date was March, 21, 2002. I was nervous – who wouldn't be when they were about to meet John the Baptist.

Huddled in my phone booth, enclosed on three sides with glass and with a narrow opening in the front, I heard nothing of the lecture or reading (I don't know what it was because I didn't hear a thing), and waited for John Edward to pick up a powerful signal, or some message from an important ghost, that directed him to the phone booth and, having discovered me, fall to his knees and welcome his brother. Again dealing with confusion about my identity, I fluctuated between saint, knight, apostle, and occasionally the Son of God. As with most in their early twenties, I did not know my place, but I was hoping that John Edward would help me determine from which star I descended. Was I a dimmer, lesser star, or the brightest in the sky.

Symptoms of schizophrenia often include delusions, including paranoid delusions during which you believe people may be out to get you, delusions of reference during which you believe things happening in the environment are directly related to you, somatic delusions, or false beliefs about your body, and delusions of grandeur, during which you may believe yourself to be special or to have special powers.

At some point, I would experience each of these characteristics of schizophrenia, although I would not be properly diagnosed with schizoaffective disorder of the bipolar type (also referred to as schizoaffective bipolar disorder) until my third hospitalization. According to the Mayo Clinic:

> Schizoaffective disorder is a condition in which a person experiences a combination of schizophrenia symptoms — such as hallucinations or delusions — and of mood disorder symptoms, such as mania or depression.

Not all experts agree that schizoaffective disorder should be treated as a distinct disorder. Some regard the condition simply as schizophrenia with some mood symptoms, while others view schizoaffective disorder as a separate disease with its own symptoms and treatments.

Untreated, people with schizoaffective disorder may lead lonely lives and have trouble holding down a job or attending school. Or, they may rely heavily on family or psychiatric group homes.

With treatment, people with schizoaffective disorder have a better prognosis than do people with schizophrenia, but not as good as people with mood disorders alone.

*Source: Reprinted from the MayoClinic.com article "Schizoaffective disorder" (www.mayoclinic.org/diseases-conditions/schizoaffective-disorder/basics/definition/con- 20029221)*

I often refer to myself as bipolar, because once you add the prefix "schizo" to any diagnosis it takes things to a whole new level of craziness. People are comfortable with bipolar because they can associate with it; they think, "this person has mood swings just like me, maybe a little more severe, but I can handle that." When you tell someone you have schizoaffective disorder they think, "this guy is one step away from wandering the street and yelling at street signs," which, as you will see, is not so far from the truth. The terms, "schizophrenia" and "schizoaffective" have a taboo all their own.

Compared to bipolar disorder, there are very few well-known individuals with schizophrenia and schizoaffective disorder.

### Famous People with Schizophrenia

- Syd Barret - the original singer for Pink Floyd, known for songs such as "Lucifer Sam" (about a cat) and "The Gnome".
- Jack Kerouac – noted beat writer who authored *On the Road*.
- John Nash – Mathematician and Nobel prize winner about whom *A Beautiful Mind* is based.
- Zelda Fitzgerald – wife of author F. Scott Fitzgerald who shares with me the fact that she was once a patient at Shepherd Pratt hospital in Towson, MD.

### Famous People with Schizoaffective disorder

- Brian Wilson of the Beach Boys
- Mary Todd Lincoln

The list of famous people with bipolar disorder is extensive. Here are a few found on various online sources:

### Actors

- Jim Carey
- Robert Downey Jr.
- Ben Stiller
- Jean-Claude Van Damme
- Robin Williams

## Artists
- Tim Burton, artist, director
- Francis Ford Coppola, director
- George Fredrick Handel, composer
- Vincent Van Gogh, painter

## Entrepreneurs
- Ted Turner, media giant

## Miscellaneous
- Buzz Aldrin, astronaut
- Larry Flynt, publisher and activist

## Musicians
- Ludwig van Beethoven
- DMX
- Ray Davies of The Kinks
- Peter Gabriel
- Jimi Hendrix
- Axl Rose of Guns n' Roses
- Sting
- Tom Waits

## Poets
- Robert Lowell
- Sylvia Plath

## Political
- Winston Churchill
- Theodore Roosevelt

**Sports**
- John Daly, golf
- Darryl Strawberry, baseball

**Writers**
- Johann Goethe
- Abbie Hoffman
- Kay Redfield Jamison, writer, psychologist
- Edgar Allen Poe
- Mark Twain
- Mark Vonnegut (Kurt Vonnegut's son)
- Virginia Woolf

It almost seems that bipolar is a good thing, and many people these days associate bipolar disorder with creativity, due in part to lists such as this. At the end of *The Count of Monte Cristo*, my favorite book, Alexandre Dumas writes in a letter from the Count to Maximilian, "there is neither happiness nor misfortune in this world, there is merely the comparison between one state and another, nothing more. Only someone who has suffered the deepest misfortune is capable of experiencing the heights of felicity." I think it is the distance between the states of happiness and misfortune that makes a person "deep." Having experienced mania, the epitome of happiness, and depression, the epitome of mental misfortune, I feel that many with bipolar disorder and other mental illnesses have a deeper understanding of life, and thus create art with deeper passion and meaning.

The "psychic" John Edward did not approach the phone booth and he did not fall to his knees and welcome me as a brother; he ended the lecture and I left the Cotillion Ball-room and returned to my hotel. I remember very little of that evening, except dinner. I went to a nearby Texas-style steak-house with yellow and red neon signs inside. I believe I ordered a burger but I can't recall vividly.

I left first thing the following morning. This is a very hazy period for me, and I have little recollection of my thoughts at the time, and I wonder if that's because I had been knocked off my high horse, so to speak, and my mania had dwindled to the point where I was thinking more clearly. If that's the case, there is nothing to remember. However, making the 1,267 mile drive in a single day, driving for approximately 18 hours, I am certain I was still manic, as such a feat, which I now refer to as "The Millennium Run" (the day I drove over 1000 miles), would only have been possible during mania. I arrived home at around 1 am, jobless and still manic.

CHAPTER

# 10

# I Awoke One Morn...

In the days following the trip to Kansas, I would compose a 44 page poem. Spending up to 8 hours a night on it, I finished in 4 days, left with a mad diatribe that was similar to Dante's *The Divine Comedy*, excepting that I, not Dante, was shown the spheres of heaven and Dante, not Virgil, was my guide. In the years that followed I would lose the floppy disk containing this poem, but not before I'd printed out a copy, which I have transcribed, embarrassingly having to reread the madness-made poetry that seemed so important, even divinely ordained, at the time.

Here is the beginning of the poem, written in quatrains (just like Nostradamus' writings), entitled "Awakening":

I awoke one morn from foggy sleep
misty dreams within my head;
Unlike most they seemed to keep
as if chiseled into lead.

My eyes were burning from break of day,
I squinted and recoiled.
It wasn't sun that lit my way
shedding light upon this toil

Was poet whose words I had rehearsed,
who'd ignited my small flame.
Many years he'd been inert
Only now to reveal his name

He smiled and stated without speaking,
"Dante was my mortal fame,
Though that's while you were sleeping.
In the waking world I have no name"

It goes on like this for 44 pages, demonstrating many old themes from my mania: images of rising above the mortal plane (which I called "transhumanizing" in the poem), time, souls as reincarnated stars, and delusional thoughts about my own importance.

At this time, my obsession with the Freemasons began, and I spent hours researching Masonic symbols and famous freemasons and seeking ways to gain membership to this secret club. I sent *Awakening* to an email address found on a mason-related website and, surprisingly, the individual behind the email address read the poem (at least some of it) and returned the comment that he liked this quatrain:

Wisdom fades as years do pass,
For children are wiser still.

As the sun turns brown green grass
Wisdom's soil is over-tilled.

It appeared that I was headed toward another hospitalization, but I started taking my pills and seeing doctors and the delusions faded away. Soon I was living life as normally as possible, but the medication, Depakote, leveled me out to the point that I had no emotion and was numb to the world.

Despite the ups and downs of my mental illness that I was experiencing, I decided to return to college, changing my major from Psychology to English with a concentration on writing, because I wanted to improve my writing technique and had aspirations of publishing *Running East* and becoming a "great writer." Throughout my enrollment I displayed an air of cockiness – being the only student to have written a book – that can only be held by those with little life experience. My thoughts turned towards my schoolwork and my delusions gave way to knowledge. Living at my parents' house and attending class during the day, I spent most of my evenings watching television in the basement, smoking marijuana in the backyard, drinking White Russians (influenced by The Dude from *The Big Lebowski*), and playing online multiplayer video games. However, that was all about to change.

I met my first girlfriend, Kelly – a friend of a friend – while drinking at a bar. I was shy; she was aggressive. She reminded me of Flora in Botticelli's *Primavera*, whose skin is the tender and soft color of peach, a rosy, blushing hue in her cheeks, eyes steel blue and seductive, strawberry-blond hair framing her face, cascading over her shoulders and down her back, with parted lips and the hint of a playful smile that exuded sexual confidence.

I will not go into the details of the relationship because this book is not about that. I will say, however, that people with mood disorders can still experience love, feeling the happiness and excitement of a new relationship, developing reliance and trust in another person, and living passion and emotions through another human being. I was gifted with all of these new experiences and, overall, I was happy; however, I continued to drink heavily, often getting into drunken arguments with my girlfriend, and many times my mood was flat and depressed.

There are such things as alcohol-induced psychotic and mood disorders, during which an alcohol abuser experiences symptoms similar to schizophrenia or bipolar disorder. Alcohol-induced disorders may occur up to one month following intoxication. According to some studies, up to forty-six percent of individuals with bipolar also have an alcohol use disorder, which is a psychiatric way to say, essentially, that almost half of the people who suffer from bipolar disorder also abuse alcohol.

I eventually moved out of my parents' house and into my girlfriend's apartment near Towson University, where I was enrolled as a full-time student. More serious about schooling, I applied myself and received good grades. However, alone one evening for the first time in months—Kelly being away—I decided to walk into Towson, a small college town filled, as college towns are, with bars.

After a half-mile walk, I stepped inside a narrow establishment with a long bar, a popcorn machine, and the permeated smell of beer and bleach. I remember the bartender well, a slender man in his fifties with sunken cheekbones and I-don't-give-a-shit-about-you eyes who seemed irritated to take my order, a pint of beer, most likely Yuengling or Bud Light. After drinking approximately four beers in an hour, I left the bar and walked up the street, where I heard music coming from a side alley. Curious, I followed the alley to a building that looked like a garage, into which flowed a stream of young people, probably around eighteen years old, of the goth/video gaming persuasion, some wearing glowing neon necklaces. Inside, someone was playing Castlevania on an old Nintendo, and I watched for a while until everyone filtered out back for a "fire show." The "fire show" consisted of a half-naked man lighting the ends of two chains on fire and twirling them around, the flaming ends of the chain moving through the air like enslaved phoenix birds attempting to fly to their freedom but perpetually drawn back to earth.

Craving a drink after the show, I asked if there was any alcohol and was told I would have to bring my own, so I headed back down the street to the original bar, where I purchased a six pack of Bud Light. On my way back to the party I ran into a young man, probably nineteen, who said he was a rapper. I asked to hear a song and as we walked up the street he recited a rap; it was okay. We reached a street corner and sat on a small wall by the street, where I opened a bottle of beer and began drinking, an act which the young man protested, and less than five minutes later a bright white light was shining on my amber-colored beer bottle and an officer was asking, "Is that your beer?" I bluntly responded, "Yes."

The officer got out of the police car and asked us to stand, and I told him that the young man was not drinking and had nothing to do with the alcohol, and the officer told him to leave. He did. Writing up a citation on a yellow piece of paper, I was asked to sign. Irate, with alcohol coursing through my blood and inflaming my normally sedate temperament, I scribbled my name illegibly. The officer, somewhat agitated although still tolerant, asked me to write my name correctly, as it was written on my license. I snatched the pen and signed more legibly, although sloppily, and dropped the pen to the ground. He handed me the citation and as I turned to walk away I said, "Your pen's on the ground."

At this point he threw me against the vehicle and proceeded to handcuff me. As I was forced inside the vehicle my head was banged against the roof of the car.

A young woman sat in the passenger seat of the cop car—blond hair and in her twenties—but I never got a good look at her because she never turned around. As we drove to the police station, only a few minutes away, I harassed the officer, asking him why he'd brought his girlfriend along with him. He did not respond to any of my taunts.

We reached the police station and my handcuffs were taken off for fingerprinting. I pressed my fingers into an ink pad and was asked one by one to create imprints of each of them. When asked to apply a finger, I held up my middle finger at the officer and asked, "This one?" To which he angrily responded, "Your index finger." I did this several times, much to the amusement of the officer who took my mug shot.

I was taken to a small cell with a metal bench that was painted green. Left there for at least thirty minutes, I used the squared edge of my handcuffs to etch "GH," my initials, into the paint. After awhile I was taken to a cell with a cot and a stainless steel toilet, where I immediately began to give the middle finger to the camera posted in the corner of the cell.

Shortly thereafter I was taken to a phone and told I had one call, so, at approximately midnight on a Friday night, I called my parents' house and told my father I had been arrested. He was disappointed and after speaking to the officer decided to let me sleep off my drunkenness in the jail, agreeing that they should release me when I sobered up. Returning to my cell, I fell asleep on the cot.

When I awoke I was released to the front of the police station by the officer who had arrested me. He was holding the remaining five beers and asked that I dump them out on the grass. I refused and walked away.

Although I'd already had a dislike of the police, thinking myself some sort of tough guy (fueled, I think, by my experiences with my *sensei* and as a martial arts instructor), now my dislike grew tenfold, and along with it my paranoia about authority in general.

Several months later I appeared in court wearing the only suit I owned and, standing in front of the courtroom, was asked to apologize to the officer, so I turned and, looking to the side of and not directly at the officer, made my apology, which was something like, "Officer – I apologize for my behavior." The officer looked to his side, as though seeking out the phantom individual I was apologizing to, and then the judge gave me twenty hours of community service at a nearby armory.

I don't want to get too far off track, so I will not go into much detail about my community service, but I will say that I swept and mopped a lot of floors and watched a lot of television with Melvin, my supervisor, on a small black and white TV in his office. Melvin was not an intelligent man, but he was a good man. He had a worn, ruddy face, blue eyes that emanated wisdom and seemed weary and compassionate at once, with a short reddish beard and strong, calloused worker's hands. He loved to talk about his Gold Wing motorcycle. One weekend he was sent to the hospital because he spent too much time in the bathtub watching television, causing him to dehydrate. As I said, he was not an intelligent man, and he loved his television.

# 11

# The End of an Era

A round this time Nick and I visited Kate in New York City, where she was interning for the Discovery Channel. Kate has big green eyes that always have the sympathetic/tired look one finds in a lover's eyes. They are deep eyes, intelligent and caring, with a gleam that signifies a passion for life and innocence, not naiveté, but a belief that there is good in a world full of good people. The green of her iris is a combination of darker forest green, emerald, and a light green that seems to jump out when she is happy about something; all surrounding a black pupil, which seems forever enclosed and untouched by the bright white of her outer eye. They were still the same eyes I had first seen in the hostel in New Orleans, and I loved her because of them.

I had once written: A young man loves a woman for looks, a fool loves a woman for her money, and a wise man loves a woman for her eyes. Of all the books, stories, and poems I've ever written, that single sentiment is the most true, because after all these years it's still accurate, and it always will be.

I barely spoke to her because I was struggling with intense feelings of love, as well as the guilt associated with having these feelings while still living with my girlfriend, Kelly. While taking the train back to Hoboken, I stared at her for a long time and eventually started to cry, the emotions too overwhelming to control. Neither she nor Nick noticed this, or addressed it anyway. Nick and I got off the train and Kate continued home. The next day we met her and her friend in Chinatown but, being completely sober, I spoke even less to her and we eventually hugged and went our separate ways. I would not see her for another five years.

Eventually I finished school and, on the day I was supposed to be walking across the stage to receive my diploma I was driving with Kelly to Key West, Florida, where Kelly and I intended to live for a year.

Key West locals, called "Conchs" after the popular local sea creature (a large snail really) of the same name, refer to the island as the two-by-four, because it is approximately four miles long and two miles wide. Supposedly, it has the greatest density of churches and bars in the country, and it also has one of the highest densities of homeless people in the nation. The sky is blue, the clouds are white, and the sea is turquoise. The air smells of saltwater and sand. It is, as the incessant playing of Jimmy Buffet songs in restaurants, bars, and shops insists, "Margaritaville." Everyone who moves there has visions of paradise, hoping to escape cold weather and whatever troubles they had, thinking, as Buffet says, "Changes in latitudes, changes in attitudes."

I served tables on weekends at a now extinct restaurant called The Sands Beach Club and worked at a Boys and Girls Club during the week, thoroughly enjoying my "job" playing basketball, video games, and dodge ball with children. After six months of nightly drinking, usually polishing off at least a bottle or two of wine each evening, I turned to Kelly and asked, "Do you want to go home," and she said, "yes." So we moved back to Baltimore.

Around this time I wrote:

### AMBULANCES

Ambulances
split the night;
sirens moaning,
lights sputtering
on dead streets
like the flames
of a gas stove

Awakened by the disturbance
I cursed those
who took my sleep -
*my* sleep

I have aged

Those sirens now
The high-pitched screams of loved ones
Trickling into deep-throated sobs
On the receiving end of phone calls
As ambulances
Speed like hope through the night

Shocking the darkness
With sight

I was maturing as a writer and as a person, but my drunken stupors also produced rage-filled poems, such as:

### EVERY FIFTEENTH SECOND

Every fifteenth second
My rage outgrows its little furnace
And I wanna chop everything in half
With the Ax of Truth

It doesn't exist, I know
But every fifteenth second
I wish it did
So I could destroy this world
And all the worldly fools...

Influenced by Langston Hughes (I had written a summary of his biography for a company similar to *Cliff Notes*), with traces of my first manic episode still lingering, I would write:

I drove to hell because I was tired of heaven
And all its grinning idiots
Who fly wingless above the world
And pretend it isn't there

Hell is real
It tastes like dirt – the detritus of life
People bear their blood soaked teeth

Which tear at others' flesh
No marshmallow here
It's not a bad taste, flesh,
If salted properly through years of heartless labor

And I see the angels buzzing around the sky
With their banners trailing behind
"Jesus saves!" reads one banner.
If I had an airplane, I'd visit Jesus too.


After my experience of believing I was the Son of God, I had now developed an overt animosity toward Jesus which revealed itself in my writing and poems. Again, this was a way of protecting myself from a manic relapse; if I disliked Jesus, I was less likely to think I *was* Jesus. Unfortunately, mania has a way of negating all willpower and creating its own train – a thundering locomotive – of thoughts that often picked up where the last episode left off.

Living in an apartment in a two-storey house, Kelly worked as a teacher for Autistic children and I tried to make it, quite unsuccessfully, as a freelance writer and editor. At this point, three years into the relationship, my interest was waning, as I think it often does. The thrill of my first relationship was becoming pedestrian and common and I began questioning it.

Enrolled in the Master of Arts in Fiction Writing program at Johns Hopkins University at the time, my paranoia would reach stifling levels whenever I was in the classroom. My breathing would become labored and I could feel my heart thudding within my chest, my blood feeling like quicksilver in my veins, cold and seeming to tickle in an uncomfortable sort of way, especially around the heart. Convinced my teacher and the other students did not like me, each class was a terrifying experience, and it didn't help that one of my classmates, an older man, wore a cap that said 'FBI' on it, which he placed on his backpack at the front of the room each class, the letters 'FBI' facing me, reminding me who was in charge.

Still in contact with Kate, although to a much lesser degree, I got drunk on a bottle of Shiraz one evening (as I often did) and, during the time I would normally spend writing, composed a long, rambling email to her in which I said I loved her.

It must have taken thirty minutes for me to hit the send button, as I knew doing so would destroy my relationship with Kelly. I weighed the benefits of my current relationship versus the potential relationship with Kate. I had a good thing going with a beautiful girlfriend who loved me, but I craved the fantasy relationship I assumed Kate could provide. I deliberated, rereading the email many times. I remember the instant I sent it; the white glow of the computer screen laying softly on my hands, as though I were in a modern heavy-chiaroscuro Baroque painting, my hands weak and unsure, placed insecurely on the black keys, my right hand hovering to the mouse, finger resting on the left button, hesitating, and then pressing "send."

Kate did not share my sentiments but, demonstrating her grace, she logically talked me out of my affection and I back-peddled, saying I was drunk when I wrote it and didn't mean it. The guilt, however, bored into me, a relentless woodpecker ticking a hole in search of bugs, and I lost all security in my relationship with Kelly. A cheater, they say, often suspects their lover of cheating. Many of us project ourselves onto others, believing they think as we do. When she was out one day I convinced myself she was at my friend's house cheating on me and I began to drive there before turning around halfway, knowing that the time had come to tell her the truth.

We were in the parking lot of a strip mall, in the car, and the moment was not particularly ripe for deep conversation, but I told her what I had done. After a short pause, she said, "that's okay." Still feeling guilty, I asked Kate to email Kelly and tell her that there was, and had been, nothing going on between us, that it had been a one-time fluke that occurred because I was drunk. She did so, but it could not save the relationship.

I don't think I will ever experience love as freshly and naively as I did then, and something about that is saddening. I'm more of a realist now; less of a romantic. A week later, Kelly started dating another man. I was filled with rage—not anger—rage. I got drunk one evening and began driving to an unknown destination, making it to nearly D.C. before calling Kelly. Pleading with her, she rejected my attempts to restore the relationship and I yelled into the phone and dropped it to the floor of the vehicle. She thought I had been in an accident. When I picked up the phone again, I told her I was coming to pick up the television, which was mine, and she said she was not at home but would be there shortly. I drove to the apartment. I sat on the dark porch. I waited for her to come home. I took my television.

Living once again with my parents, I drove nightly on Loch Raven Drive, a stretch of county road skirting the banks of Loch Raven Reservoir, one of the main water supplies for Baltimore, which is located about ten miles north of the city. It is a dark road, with elms and oaks climbing high on either side, their boughs illuminated by the headlights as a vehicle passes, the light on the trees contrasting with the black of the forest, closing in on the car, so the road is all there is—black asphalt with an endless row of yellow hash marks in the center, passing by like lights on the ceiling of a hospital hallway.

The road twists and turns abruptly, and it takes concentration and skill, often requiring sudden stops as indifferent deer cross the road. One evening, I made the drive drunk.

Driving with greater speed than normal, listing over the center lines, the music blaring, my eyes dosing, thoughts of Kelly and Kate occupying my mind, I stopped in the parking lot next to the dam.

The dam is 101 ft. tall and located at the top of a hill. Beside the dam is a scramble of white, medium-sized quartz rocks. I walked to these rocks and lay down, my hands behind my head, looking into the distant sky, seeing my old friends—the stars—looking back at me. For some time I had not thought manic thoughts, and I did not think them now. Instead, I reflected on my life but, although I waited for it, I did not have a life-changing epiphany.

I began considering suicide, writing at a later point:

Today is a suicide day. I call them suicide days because I spend many moments throughout the day thinking about my death. I feel hopeless and lost, and I cannot imagine happy times, recalling only other suicide days. I lay in bed for hours at a time, crying some days, sleeping others, and always thinking of the best manner in which to kill myself. Not wanting to trouble my loved ones with misery, I think of suicides that look like accidents, such as driving my car into a tree or falling from a cliff whilst climbing it.

It is especially saddening to think of your own funeral. Not because you see yourself in a coffin being lowered into the stiff soil, but because you see your loved ones weeping or standing stoically with quivering jaws. While this is a terrible thought, it always brings a sort of satisfaction, as you think that you have in fact made some impact on the world. You are also pleased by the fact that others are sharing your pain, and you no longer feel so lonely in your sadness. You recover for a moment, wiping tears from your eyes, blowing your nose, and sitting up in bed as though you're prepared to face a new day. This renewed hope lasts only a few moments, and again you lie in bed contemplating your suicide. This seesawing goes on all day – hope then despair, hope then despair, hope then despair, always longer periods of despair – until you are so exhausted that you forgo both hope and despair and sit numbly on the couch watching television and thinking how lazy and worthless you are.

Soon after I would plan to kill myself.

# 12

# A Trip

The following story is true—I wrote it shortly after the incident it discusses.

I filled a small backpack with a ragged cotton beach towel, a half-empty box of waterproof matches, three plastic water bottles, and a Leatherman multi-tool and exited my parents' house without intending to return.

It was 4 p.m. The sun paced its monotonous course along the sky, gaining speed as it fell toward the distant horizon. It was a summer sky. The color of a faded robin's egg with bleached white clouds where the elements had scraped away all signs of life. I had seen such an egg the previous day, beneath the splintering wooden porch in the backyard; the egg had fallen and split into two nearly identical vessels. The yolk, dried into a golden yellow crisp, hung waveringly between the shattered ovum and a razor-thin blade of grass. Above, a desolate bird's nest drooped its scruffy hips around a wooden crossbeam. Climbing the porch, I examined the interior of the nest; it was empty except for a few clumps of hardened mud used to hold the nest together.

I felt the sensation of drowning when I stepped from the air-conditioned house and into the sultry late-afternoon air; my pores constricted, my arm hairs stood on end, and my throat swallowed a warm gulp of heavy atmosphere. This sensation repeated when I sat in the driver's seat of my silver Mitsubishi Gallant, though I got the feeling of greater depth as the imprisoned air pressed sadistically on my chest, sucking the air from my lungs and providing barely enough oxygen to breathe.

I drove westward, where the sun, muffled by the halo of the day's extreme heat, burned a tangerine-colored hole in the atmosphere.

The highway ran west from Baltimore at seventy miles per hour. I recall passing a laughing couple in a blue Honda Accord with a "Mean People Suck" bumper sticker. Her red hair whipping playfully against dove-white skin, a woman was driving with the window down. I imagined that her laughter leapt out her window and mingled around the hollow silver exterior of my vehicle. The laugh stopped outside my grime-speckled window, peered in with a wide white grin that froze a moment before it dwindled into a pathetic smile with phony up-turned edges, dropped to the highway, and passed, flipping and wrenching like an out-of-water fish, into the rear-view mirror. It seemed at that moment that all happy things were falling behind me, left on the black pavement like an empty Fritos bag, useless, lifting and falling with the wind, loosed from any purpose or meaning: empty. Existing only as film in an unwatched movie, my good memories seemed to melt away, as old movie film sometimes melted, the flickering frames bubbling and then snapping. The bad memories, however, seemed immediate: the madness, the hospitalization, the break up with my girlfriend. And these memories replayed in sequence, a mad loop of obsessive thought, connected by the emotion of despair – the emotion I was feeling then – as our memories sometimes seem triggered by corresponding emotions.

Despair: a helpless feeling experienced at a time when one feels little self worth, sees little good in the world, and believes there is no way out. Despair is like standing in a dirt hole, the edge of which is just out of jumping reach; you see beautiful blue sky above and attempt to climb but find no footing, you yell and are not heard, you cry and are not heard, your tongue sticks to the roof of your mouth in thirst, your stomach pinches and twists with hunger, you feel the skin tighten where tears have dried on your face. And then night approaches.

My ex-girlfriend returned a call I had made earlier, and we had a trivial conversation: "why did you call?" I hoped speaking with her would change my mind; it did not.

After forty-five minutes of driving, I exited the overcrowded thoroughfare and was soon at the trailhead. When I exited my car, the sun was nearly dead. I grabbed the backpack from the backseat and paced toward the trail, stopping to pluck a yellow honeysuckle flower from its wiry bush. The honeysuckle flower had no taste when I licked it; the nectar had evaporated.

I traveled toward the trail via an abandoned, cracked, and weed-overgrown road that was cut short by a rusted guardrail with small flakes of silver paint clinging to brown-encrusted metal. I followed a set of ghostly white footprints which served as a directional guide to the trail. The footprints expired at a smooth, almond-colored dirt trail.

The Appalachian Trail hooked past the highway that I'd been driving on minutes before and into the forest, which had already begun to lose its colors just as pictures, over time, lose theirs. I walked beneath the highway overpass, the "whoomp, whoomp, whoomp" of rubber tires obnoxiously loud. A tractor-trailer passed and a balmy gust of gritty air throttled past me, flapping my shirtsleeves before whining, screaming, and finally curling up into the shadowy corner of the overpass.

I soon crossed into the woods and was overcome with the light awareness of leaving all "that" behind.

The trees watched silently.

With the nearly weightless pack, I traveled briskly, easily climbing the first difficult section of "The Trail" with indifference. As I crossed into a clearing – a fifty-foot-wide incision created for the phone lines climbing wearily up the mountain– I slowed to observe the Western horizon. The sky blushed, perhaps out of fear of the night, perhaps out of anger at the loss of its bauble.

The woods drifted into sleep; the cadence of her warm breath became rhythmic and, as she gently caressed the smooth leaves of the oaks and sumacs that rested upon her chest, they sighed tenderly, remembering. Creatures that had remained hidden throughout the day crept from their hiding places, crawling, hopping, and flying through the unwatched woods. High-pitched, throaty chirps emerged from beneath the blanket of descending darkness.

I was startled by a black toad as it hopped out of my way and rested on its fat, fleshy belly beside the trail, elbows outward, front feet splayed, watching me through its large, bulbous black eyes as I continued with a determined pace down the darkening trail.

Eager to find the overlook that was my destination, I scoured, with squinting eyes, the western side of the ridge. My failing sight forced me to retrieve my glasses from the backpack. I placed them on my head and was granted a final, artificial lucidity.

Pushing timidly into the darkness of the forest, I pressed forward irrationally towards my fate, sucked towards the heavy granite cliffs like a piece of driftwood in a rising tide. My feet crunched heavily on the dead leaves underneath. I followed the half-light and was soon ascending a small hill and stepping onto the flat cliff of the overlook, crossing from the nearly black woods into the murky night.

I had missed the Armageddon of sunset, but remnants of the battle remained: smoke seemed to emanate from the earth, rising toward the dim first stars and wrapping the expansive valley in a grey-blue veil.

The highway was a mechanical thread trundling toward the west, kept alive by an endless two-way conveyor belt of crawling steel insects, some bright-eyed, some angry. They traveled in their vehicles, listening to their music, bobbing their heads, offering their singing to the indifferent night. They passed away; I cared not for the loss.

I sat down cross-legged on the rock overlook, running my hand across the thick stone. Tiny, smooth basins and divots, created by millennia of thunderstorms and draughts, pocked the warm surface. I brushed a stone from the cliff face and it ricocheted through the nettles of a pine tree and landed with a loud snap on a boulder far below.

Time froze. I sat on the rock, considered my life, and contemplated my death. Years ago, I had dreamed of proposing to my future wife on those rocks, now, I had decided to end my life on them. I fluctuated between determination and sorrow, weeping, drying my tears, and weeping again, thinking of my funeral, of who would be there, of how sad they would be. Sitting cross-legged as though a yogi in meditation, lying on my back to look at the dim stars, peering over the edge of the cliff, I postponed my death as long as possible.

My cell phone began to ring and I saw that it was my mother but when I answered no one was there and the reception was gone. Because I had been looking for omens, signs that I should continue my life, I took this as a divine message that I should not give up. But, within minutes, I had once again dropped into despair.

When one is about to commit suicide, and I have pondered this numerous times, the thing that saves a person is thinking about the pain their death will cause others. I imagine that those who actually go through with it are the ones who believe that no one will feel pain at their death, or who want to "get back" at others by creating that pain for them.

Sitting alone on that rock ledge, I became selfish, thinking about how horrible my life was and how easy it would be for it to be over. The misery finally overcomes the compassion towards loved ones: that is how people can do it. And so I lie on my back, feeling the warmth of the stone and taking in the celestial vista for what seems to be the final time.

Suddenly I was bitten on the back by an ant. As the reader know by now, I have always been fascinated by ants and they have great significance to me. I sat up abruptly and immediately believed I had received another omen, that a greater being was expressing its disapproval of my suicide through a tiny messenger, and that it was time for me to go.

I returned to the dark forest, unable, after the first twenty yards, to see where I was placing my feet. For a moment, I stopped and glanced back through the woods toward the overlook. The trees, bushes, and granite were silhouetted on the gray lightboard of the sky. The forest ahead seemed to descend into the oblivion of suffocating night while behind me was a vague, yet definitive line where partial light was overtaken by black. Passing my right arm above this line, a thin, straight shadow was cast on the forest floor directly beneath me; as the shadow crossed the threshold, my hand became the infinite darkness enshrouding the unknown distance of my own future.

———

I realize now that the trip to the overlook had really been about pitting my life against the life of a greater being, testing that being and trying to elicit some sort of response. At the time, I felt I had received that response and as a result felt an overwhelming sense of spiritualism. I began to clap rhythmically, as parishioners in some churches might clap, the hollow claps echoing through the forest.

Several times I stumbled into trees, but somehow I found the trail and, in the blackness, began hiking southward. After a while my eyes become accustomed to the night and I could see almost as though it were day.

I walked for two miles then saw three lights dancing above the trail.

I said in a loud voice, "I'm coming up behind you, don't be scared."

The lights paused as in silent deliberation. It was a group of three – two teenagers and an older male who, by his green, matching attire, appeared to be some sort of counselor. Each had a beam of light emanating from a cycloptic headlamp.

"Nice night for a walk," the counselor said.

I agreed, looking the counselor in the face and seeing only the lower portion of his chin; the rest of his face was covered in light. My black pupils constricted, pulling taught the drum of my hazel irises.

Behind me I heard one of the teenagers say, "How can you see?"

I continued walking, saying over my shoulder, "after forty-five minutes you get night vision."

Continuing past the group, my night vision was hindered for a few minutes by their light and I several times stumbled off the trail, once stepping into the jagged tooth of a thorn bush, which sliced a crescent-shaped cut into my slender right calf muscle. Sweat immediately surged into the wound; miniscule crystals of salt ate at the fleshy walls. I tended to the wound, first pouring water on it then pressing firmly upon it with my hand. The gentle swishing of a medium-sized brook filled the silence and I again felt the sensation of being underwater. This time, however, the sensation was not confining – I felt myself to be a natural part of the surroundings.

Through the swaying branches and sweeping black leaves, the moon watched patiently. The forest stilled; the high-pitched, trilling chirps of cicadas and rustle of decaying leaves ceased; the breeze seemed respectful of the moment, hushing and kneeling reverently in prayer on the forest floor. I observed the deep blue creases in the moon's soft, milk-white skin. In place of the melancholy that normally came with such moments, I recalled a fact from Astronomy class: the darkness of the moon is merely the shadow of the earth; the light of the moon is created by the reflection of the sun. Even at night, I thought, the sun still shines.

After another mile, I stepped onto the solid asphalt of the road which, from this direction, connected to route 40, then to another road, then another, then intertwined with 70, which flowed to Baltimore, then intersected 95, which traveled to Philadelphia and then New York, where I imagined the city, pulsing with light and life. I smelled the sweetness of honeysuckle and, nearing my car, noticed the dim residue of ghostly painted footprints walking in the opposite direction.

Probably many people have had bad days when they say in passing, "I wish I were dead." The difference between "bad days" (or even a string of bad days) and the truly suicidal is sitting in a bathtub, staring for a long time at the blue veins running up your wrist, pressing on them with your finger, watching the blood back up, the blue a grayish blue, wondering, as the water becomes cold, where you can find a razorblade, wondering if it will hurt as it slices into the skin, wondering who will attend your funeral. You release your finger, the blood in the vein surging homeward, returning to your heart, polluted, soon to be cleaned, renewed, and pumped vigorously into an artery, leading to another artery, then another, connecting with the lungs, traveling through muscle, pulsing into the brain and giving life to hope somewhere in the depth of darkness.

There is one song that has always helped me through my own bad days: David Bowie's "Rock 'n' Roll Suicide", which repeats the line "You're not alone."

David Bowie knows the secret to walking away from suicide. If, in your darkest hour, you imagine the pain that your death will cause those who care about you, and if there is always someone who cares about you, then you can talk yourself out of it. Ultimately, suicide is a selfish act. In the end it is better to suffer in this life than to make those you love suffer as much as you have. Depression always has an end. Always.

CHAPTER

# 13

# The Green Light

In F. Scott Fitzgerald's *The Great Gatsby,* Jay Gatsby stares out across the bay behind his enormous mansion at a single point of green light in the darkness of the evening, the light belonging to the dock of his longed-for love, Daisy. While some may argue this light is hope, I believe it is more accurately the destiny we hope for but can never obtain. In the novel, Gatsby is unable to win Daisy despite every conceivable effort and accomplishment. In my reality, Kate is my Daisy.

After the breakup with Kelly I emailed Kate more frequently and was more in love, or more obsessed, with her than I had ever been. I kept this a secret from her, acting under the pretense of "just a friend," but I desperately desired something deeper between us.

Soon after the breakup I got a job at a temp agency. I was first placed as a receptionist for two days and then as a worker at a non-profit organization. I still remember the smell of the place, like carpet and keyboards. I quit the temp job to work at a publishing company where I was paid ten dollars an hour and assigned to a room consisting of three long tables, with five new recruits at each table pecking away at computers. I truly felt that I had become one of the faceless sheep I wrote about in *Running East*. Amidst absolute, uncomfortable silence and clicking keyboard keys, my paranoia returned and I often felt people were talking about me, and felt a great deal of claustrophobia in the "computer farm." I had become my own fictional hero, Soco Killman. One day, fed up with the monotony and claustrophobia, I wrote an "I quit" note on a tiny Post-It pad, the only paper I could find, stuck it on my boss's desk, and walked out. Since then I have not worked for anyone other than myself. This incident oddly reflects one of the endings in *Running East*, in which Soco leaves his job and runs toward the sunrise, albeit no running was involved in the real-life incident.

The following short excerpts were written during that time period and reflect my thinking.

This is about the aforementioned road:

It is a winding road that travels through the woods, along the water and beneath the oaks and maples. I have driven it many times and know it by heart. During the day it is well traveled, with cars parked along its widest part, where there is a small grassy area next to the water. At night, the road is silent and dark, and your headlights peer impotently into the blackness, illuminating the yellow line in the center of the road and the boughs of the first row of trees. Many times there are deer along the road, and they lift their heads and perk their ears as you approach, sometimes bounding off into the forest, sometimes staring big-eyed as you pass and then returning their noses to the grass. I like to hang my left arm out the window and feel the cool evening air against my skin. In the spring it smells like honeysuckle; late summer it smells like green leaves; fall it smells like dead leaves; winter it smells like frozen dirt.

This excerpt recalls the end of my relationship with Kelly:

She was once beautiful to me, and she is still beautiful, but not to me. All I see when I think of her are the dimples of fat on the back of her thighs.

I can feel the relationship fading away. It's been fading since the day I looked at her when she came home and I wasn't happy to see her or mad about an incident that had happened earlier, I was indifferent. It was like looking at the face of a stranger passing on the street. Her eyes were solid and reminded me of a wrecking ball crashing through the final circular remnant of a topaz-colored wall. Beyond the wall was grey air. Her nose was too wide, her chin was too pointy, her hair was too thin, and she looked very similar to someone whom I've never met.

"How was work?" I asked.

The following excerpts represent my own thoughts and feelings at the time, as I struggled with the normal emotions of growing up and the realization that I am mortal and perhaps not super-special or super human. The references to places and individuals are fiction, but the rest is real:

I am average. There is nothing special about me: I do not have a great personality, I'm not strong, or short, or fast, and I haven't been anywhere interesting. I stare at a computer screen all day then I shuffle through crowds, nudging my way past other average people on my way home to my common apartment. The universe will not stop without me – when I die the energy from my body will dissipate into other things - worms will eat me and shit me out and my energy will help fertilize the soil. There is nothing I can do to change this.

It's amazing how many times a person can check his email in a day. For me, it must be over one hundred times. That's about once every five minutes. I don't actually want to receive any emails, at least not ones asking me to do something. Emails make me feel important, like somebody wants to pay me special attention. It takes energy to create an email.

My ex girlfriend found my replacement one week after we broke up after a four-year relationship. She knew I was average. He is built like a body builder – I'm built like a pear with a stick stuck through the middle and a grape on top.

According to Wikipedia the equation says that mass and energy are the same thing. I weigh about 175 pounds. My mass times 3×108 m/s (the speed of light) equals the amount of energy I produce. The smaller the matter the more energy it produces. An atom, for instance, will result in an atomic explosion when it is split in half. If I am split in half my innards will plop onto the ground and blood will spray everywhere and I will be on the news. They will say, "A man was split in half today by a samurai sword," and then they'll do a small report, and that's about it. Some people may go to work the next day and say, "did you hear about the guy who was split in half?" but the day after that it will be old news. If something as small as an atom is split in half you hear about it for years.

Energy cannot be created or destroyed. I can be destroyed by a car crash, bullet, heart attack, etc.

Frank works in the cubicle next to mine, and he is interesting. I think he shits fireworks. His energy is transferred into kite surfing, rock climbing, and conversations with his many friends. The heat from my body, which is a form of energy called thermal energy, is transferred into couches and chairs.

Sometimes I am jealous of famous people. They remind me of my insignificance. They walk down streets and people stop to take their pictures. I walk down streets and people shove me in the shoulder or ignore me completely.

There are about 6 billion 900 million people in the world. It would take 220 years to count to 6.9 billion, assuming you counted one number per second. Each of those seconds represents a human, I represent 1 second. 1 second in 220 years.

I can smell Frank's cologne from here. I smell it all day long, wafting over the wall of my cubicle and poisoning my air. People wear cologne so they will get attention. Sometimes I wear aftershave.

There are people who are passionate about things. Green Peace volunteers confront massive whaling boats because they care dearly about the whales' lives. People volunteer to help the sick and dying in Africa. I envy their passion because I have none. Although I do not consider myself a nihilist, it is entirely possible that I believe in nothing. I want to believe in something, I really do, but I can't make myself believe in something. I think there are people who make themselves believe in something because it makes them more interesting or because it gives them direction.

At some point I became the guy you feel sorry for, the guy you invite to parties because you feel like you should.

I want to write about the average man because he is most interesting to me. He is real and the epitome of the human condition. Great and interesting men are entertaining, but they are novelties. I do not want people to read what I have written and say, "I want to be like that," I want them to say, "I am like that, and I am not alone."

CHAPTER

# 14

# Chameleon

Eventually, after some failed dating attempts on an online dating service, I met a woman named Jessie in a bar and we began dating. I drank every time I was with her and I do not remember a single day that year in which I did not drink. Continuing to work as a freelance writer and editor, I got odd jobs as though I were a writing and editing handyman hammering my keyboard and fixing dangling participles and run-on sentences, reconstructing shoddy, self-imploding paragraphs, and constructing new articles from miscellaneous information I'd picked up on the internet. My crowning achievement of this period was a lurid (and fictional!) piece entitled "77 Sex Tips Men can Learn from Lesbians," I picked up any job I could find, including writing travel articles for a Key West vacation guide and ghostwriting a novel in which the Nazis invaded the United States. After writing a few chapters, I insisted that the plot was implausible and was removed from the project.

It was October again. The leaves were changing and the World Series would soon be on television. I stopped taking my pills.

It is difficult to understand why a person with a mental illness stops taking their pills. One would think if you were stranded in the ocean you'd keep your life vest on, the pills acting to keep you above water, to keep you from drowning. But you see something below, a fish or shell, and you want to dive down to get a better view, so you unclip your vest—just for a minute—and dive. Suddenly, you aren't sure which way is up . . . and it begins.

I was living in a friend's house at the time, paying rent for a small bedroom on the first floor, in which I had a mattress which lay directly on the floor and a dresser with some clothes in it. There was a kitchen table in the main room, which had colorfully painted walls and bookshelves, and I sat there most of the day working on miscellaneous writing and editing jobs.

Manic episodes can often be triggered by stress, and at the time I was experiencing great amounts of stress because it was unlikely I'd be able to pay my rent. Although it always appeared subtly in crowded areas or social situations, the paranoia began creeping further into my life, dragging itself toward me like a legless zombie, eyes grey and wide, as I, paralyzed by fear, waited for it to bite me and spread its madness.

Continuing my obsession with the Freemasons, I began obsessively researching the organization on the internet; and once again the hierarchy of stars began assembling itself within my mind. Coincidences again became destiny, and I became more important.

I lived only an hour from Washington, D.C., and I learned that that the layout of our nation's capital exhibits numerous symbols of the Freemasons, including a pentagram and an eye-shaped area at the Naval Observatory. I know this because I spent hours studying maps of the city and identifying Freemason sites and symbols. Atop the capitol building is a statue of Lady Freedom, which was refurbished and returned to its nest above the dome in 1993 amidst much ceremony—Liza Minnelli sang "America the Beautiful" and Poet Rita Dove composed a poem called *Lady Freedom Among Us.* Believing the title of this poem to be a Freemason symbol, I shifted the letters around until I was left with the words "Lady Freemason."

The theme of reincarnation again surfaced in my mind and I began thinking that the Freemasons were a society going back to ancient Egypt that was designed for high-ranking returning souls. I studied Egyptology, discovering that the three pyramids of Giza align with the three stars in the constellation Orion's belt, and I felt that ancient Egyptian kings manipulated the soul hierarchy by associating their tombs—the pyramids—with three of the brightest, and therefore most powerful, stars in the sky. I studied Egyptian pharaohs and soon believed that they were blocking my transcendence because they had put a kink in the hierarchy and would not allow me to pass by their stars.

As always, the mania started with some intriguing fact—the interesting patterns found in the layout of DC— that fused with another interesting fact—the pyramids' alignment with the stars—that led to something else, and something else, and so on until the snowball of mania was rumbling downhill toward Hell at breakneck speed.

During my research on the Freemason, I was introduced to the Illuminati, and then became obsessed with the famous secret society at Yale University, *Skull and Bones*, associating Kate, who had attended Oxford, with this society. I became extremely paranoid that the members of this society were out to get me, and I thought that Kate had all these years been toying with me, using me, a pathetic, weak, middle-class American, as fodder for her insider jokes.

From my experience, delusions of grandeur come before paranoid delusions, as if the paranoid delusions were a natural defense mechanism triggered by power, or, in this case, imagined power from imagined greatness. I believe this mimics actual power, as I think the more power a person has the more paranoid they become. Certainly, the President of the United States is more paranoid than Joe who works in a retail store down the street. With great power, imagined or real, comes great responsibility...and increased paranoia.

My second manic episode was less coherent than the first. Thoughts were more rapid and the period between the initial onset and entering the mental hospital was only a few weeks, as opposed to months.

I became obsessed with the notion that people were trying to steal my power or keep me from attaining my true rank in the hierarchy of souls. Studying the famous philosophers, physicists, and mathematicians pictured in the *School of Athens*, a painting by Raphael that my father had in his office, I began to see it as a guide for the hierarchy of souls. The painting includes Plato (pictured as Leonardo Da Vinci), Aristotle, and a self-portrait of Raphael himself peeking out of the bottom right corner. One particular image, an evil-

looking man in a crimson robe, points downward. I thought
he represented the devil, or possibly Nostradamus.

One moment I was being hazed to become a member of
the *Skull and Bones*, the next I was being stalked, harassed,
and belittled by the same organization. I floundered wildly
with my beliefs, again losing all sense of time and morality
and fluctuating from absolutely moral to amoral, believing
myself one moment to be Jesus and the next Lucifer. According to MDGuidelines.com:

> Mania occurs because of an imbalance in brain chemicals
> called neurotransmitters. Manic episodes usually have a
> rapid onset, building suddenly over a few days. The epi-
> sodes last a few weeks to several months. They often are
> preceded by difficulty sleeping. Impaired sense of reality
> (psychotic features) can occur during mania. The indi-
> vidual may see visions, hear voices, or fixate upon untrue
> beliefs (delusions). The psychosis is usually consistent
> with the individual's sense of extraordinary wellbeing.
> Grandiose delusions are common, such as the individual
> believing he is a genius or of noble birth.

Neurotransmitters were the problem. They were supposed
to be sending signals across synapses. According to Eric
Chudler, Ph.D of the University of Washington:

> Communication of information between neurons is accom-
> plished by movement of chemicals across a small gap called
> the synapse. Chemicals, called neurotransmitters, are re-
> leased from one neuron at the presynaptic nerve terminal.

G.H. FRANCIS

Neurotransmitters then cross the synapse where they may be accepted by the next neuron at a specialized site called a receptor. The action that follows activation of a receptor site may be either depolarization (an excitatory postsynaptic potential) or hyperpolarization (an inhibitory postsynaptic potential). A depolarization makes it MORE likely that an action potential will fire; a hyperpolarization makes it LESS likely that an action potential will fire.

I don't know exactly what depolarization means, but I know how it feels. It feels like the world has become an enormous terrarium, the hobby of some omniscient being that has attached a special string to you so that it may monitor you closely and toy with you, as a sadistic person does with a dog, placing enticing things in front of you and pulling them away, oppressing you with unbearable physical and mental torture, lifting you up, pulling you into the atmosphere of the terrarium, bringing you near the lip, allowing you to trace your fingertips along the edges and feel the cool air of freedom, before dropping you to the ground, the force breaking your legs or burying you beneath piles of dirt and rock. Near the edge the air is light and ethereal-intoxicating and drug-like. Beneath the rock you cannot breathe and the air is heavy and thick with dust, stifling and draining. You are either far above or far below the world.

Because destiny mandated that my chemicals were not moving properly across their synapses, I believed that Khufu was blocking my rightful ascension into my place amongst the stars. As I've mentioned, legend has it that the three pyramids of Giza were designed to correlate with the three stars in Orion's belt. With each of these pyramids acting as a tomb, this fit perfectly into my scheme of the soul/star hierarchy, and it was apparent to me that the Egyptian pharaohs were well aware of this hierarchy. I had, during my previous relationship with Kelly, purchased a star as a gift for about sixty dollars. It seemed like a reasonable price for something ten times the size of the Earth, and I named it "The Hammock," where Kelly and I had spent our first night together. The Hammock happened to be located down and to the right of easternmost star in Orion's belt, Mintaka. If the pyramids lined up with the stars in Orion's belt, the location of my star, purchased years before this incident, would correlate with the location of the Sphinx in Giza.

Although it has the body of a lion, the Sphinx's head is suspected by some to represent the head of Khafra, a fourth dynasty pharaoh and the successor to Khufu, who has the largest pyramid at Giza. In addition to being represented on the Sphinx, Khafra's tomb is the second largest pyramid in the complex of Giza, while Menkaura's is the smallest.

My power lust during my manic episodes was unquenchable and, feeling I had not attained my rightful position among the stars or my rightful position in this life, I suspected that I had been sabotaged in some way and believed that another ruler had placed my head on an animal to limit my ascension. I soon began to think that the bodies of myself and my real father, Khufu, had been locked in enormous pyramids to stop our ascension, and that the intentional placement of the pyramids along Orion's belt was designed to project us to those stars, which were not our natural positions, during our next cycle of life. For days I researched and eventually became certain that Ramses II was the culprit.

Again, staying up all hours of the night, working on my computer with only the small light of a desktop lamp illuminating the small room, I ate infrequently and only left my room to use the bathroom.

At the time, I wrote:

### CHAMELEON

Eaten by flies
He could not hold
Their faceted eyes

Their eyes
Their eyes
Their eyes

Too much to see
Not enough to eat
His stomach burst
And the flies broke freee
Feasted on his bumpy flesh

His eyes
His eyes
His eyes

Never focused
On a single sight
The only thing he understood
Was darkness found at night

Chameleon
Eaten by prey

Cause no analysis will
Take their souls away.

"Chameleon" seems to foreshadow the coming paranoia and also focuses on a creature that is able to change, able to take on different faces, much as I felt I was able to do.

I continued to work on my freelance projects, or attempted to. At the time I was helping a friend transcribe listings from a medical dictionary to a Word document. However, I soon suspected my friend of being a conspirator attempting to hold me from my rightful ascension. I believed the listings of medical illnesses and body parts were designed to confine me to my physical body, reminding me that I was human and therefore depriving me of my immortality.

I saw that we are all born into this world completely innocent, and started seeing power as a tangible thing, divided into words, the words taking my own power and dividing it amongst certain sources. The medical book and all its terms, for instance, belonged to the power of doctors, who would be ruled by a great star, although I cannot remember which. I believed that all humans were originally immortal, as it was in the Garden of Eden, but that we had been told lies to take this immortality from us. One of the chief lies was that we could get sick and that our bodies died. Once we heard this, it became true. Doctors, therefore, were the greatest sinners of all because they took our immortality, and it didn't help that the Caduceus—the symbol of medicine—had two snakes on it, the symbol of the devil. My father is a doctor and my mother is a nurse. I believed they were foster parents ascribed by the forces of evil to ensure that I would not attain my rightful rank as savior.

With these thoughts went the appropriate devastating emotions. Losing all trust in my own parents, who are the foundations of my world outlook, I lost trust in everything else, from family and friends, to societies, to political structures. They were the two pillars that held up everything, and I believed they had deceived me my entire life. It wasn't true, but it was my reality, and in our individual realities we create our own truths, no matter how false they may be externally. The anger and confusion that goes along with finding out my parents were not my actual parents, and had been poisoning me my entire life, was real, if only to me.

Only after losing trust in my parents did I understand how important it is to have a strong, reliable parental bond. Because of that bond, I have always had a place to call home, as well as the security that comes with it. If an individual with a mental disorder doesn't have a stable person or thing they can always trust and rely on, it's easy to lose bearings, because they have nothing to navigate back to. From my experience, stability is the most important factor in managing a mental disorder, and, as much as it is the responsibility of the individual with the disorder to live a stable life by not abusing drugs or alcohol and by taking their pills, it is the responsibility of their loved ones to ensure that they have the appropriate environment to foster that stability.

Once again, during this manic episode, morality swung dramatically from the moral to the amoral, and I soon began thinking that all power was actually a natural balance, and that it was intended to be divided amongst both the good and the evil. With this reasoning I lumped pharmacists and drug dealers into a single group, considering neither evil, and believing both to have a rightful piece of the power pie. Writers and poets had power because of their words and were in a group all their own. Architects had their power, Painters theirs, politicians theirs, etc.

The final poem I wrote before my hospitalization was:

### BREAKING FREE

The darkest place
The empty side
of an empty face

The days and thoughts from this time mix together, and I am not certain of the order of events, but know I spent a great amount of time researching Egyptian pharaohs and philosophers, among others, because I was attempting to piece together the proper hierarchy of souls. Again, any two things or ideas, no matter how different, could blend together to form a single thought. Nothing was impossible or disconnected.

During this time I drove to my girlfriend Jessie's house and sat on her bed watching television for two days straight. The television spoke to me, each program a message intended for me. When I say, "my television spoke to me," I do not mean it addressed me directly. I still heard what the individuals on television were saying just as a sane person would hear, only my perception was that they were saying these things for my sake and my sake only, fully aware that I was watching the program. It was as if I was an observer sitting in the same room as them, my presence affecting what they did and did not say.

After my girlfriend served me butternut squash soup in bed, I decided to take a shower, remembering vividly that I believed myself to be Hermes, messenger of the gods and owner of the Caduceus. I believed I had an important message that must be delivered immediately to Zeus. I remember the clear shower curtain with green and blue polka dots, and I remember the warm water washing over my face, and I remember the sense of urgency I felt and the arrogance of feeling like a god, feeling as though I were above everyone else.

I often wonder where these thoughts came from, if they are inherent deep within us or simply the result of madness. Does each of us somewhere deep inside feel that we are special and above all others? Is there some remnant of our infancy, when we received the attention of the world, dormant within us, subdued only by politeness and common courtesy?

In 1914 Sigmund Freud wrote a paper called "On Narcissism: An Introduction", which outlined the concept of primary narcissism, a theory that all infants go through a phase which, according to Christian Hubert, is a "primal state where id, ego, and external world are not differentiated" (http://www.ehow.com/facts_6144550_primary-narcissism_.html). One of the signifiers of adult narcissism is "Fantasies of fame, power and success. Belief in their superiority over others."

Was I experiencing inflated narcissism? Did I, as I suspect and believe, degenerate to an earlier period in my life (perhaps the wrong synapses fired in my brain, leading the train tracks of my mind to old, long forgotten realms) and begin to view things from the eyes of my infancy?

According to Sam Vaknin, author of *Malignant Self Love - Narcissism Revisited*, "the manic phase of bipolar I disorder is often misdiagnosed as Narcissistic Personality Disorder." According to one of my therapists, the *DSM V* lists mood disorders on a sliding scale. Imagine a rainbow of colors, with each color representing a mood disorder. In the *DSM IV*, blue may represent bipolar and yellow social anxiety disorder. In the *DSM V*, or so I understand, the colors can be mixed and matched, so that any one disorder can blend with another, creating diverse, unique colors for each individual with a mood disorder, the resulting color from the previous example being green and representing no specific disorder. The colors would be so varied that individual names could not be given to each grouping.

However, in this instance I believe it was more than a mixing of disorders. There seemed to be an absence of ego, as I was constantly shifting from one persona to another, "taking faces from the ancient gallery" as Jim Morrison sang in the famous song by the Doors.

Jim Morrison witnessed a terrible car accident when he was a child, viewing the dead bodies of Native Americans as they lay strewn across a highway. From that point on, Morrison believed that one of the souls of the dead Native Americans, a shaman, entered his own. Immortalized in *Wayne's World* is the naked Indian Morrison is said to have seen in his dreams.

In *An American Prayer*, Morrison talks about an accident on the highway, resulting in some dead Native Americans, one of whose soul jumped into his own.

I knew then that Morrison believed in the soul hierarchy and believed he was completely cognizant of the power scale.

Power could be disseminated in any number of ways but the most potent manner was to occupy individuals' minds, and the more minds one affected, the more powerful they became in the hierarchical sense. Morrison was loved by tens of thousands, if not hundreds of thousands or millions, of women, and his half naked photograph still influences women of this generation, thereby ensuring, I believed, the continuation of his power.

Morrison also referred to himself as "The Lizard King" and, expanding my hierarchy, I soon believed that dominance of the world was divided into animal kingdoms based on the five main vertebrate animal kingdoms of mammal, fish, bird, amphibian, and reptile. Each of these has a peak species that is at the top of the food chain. Morrison, being the Lizard King, was at the top of the reptile kingdom and he represented T-Rex, which I believed to be the king of all lizards. In *All the Young Dudes*, David Bowie sings, "Oh, man I need TV when I got T. Rex." This came as a sign to me that Bowie and Morrison were on the same team, that of music and art, and they were backing me in my rise to power.

In continual search of myself, I found new answers in television. On October 18, 2006, at approximately 12:00 am, Jennifer Love Hewitt and Tim Burton were on *The Tonight Show* with Jay Leno. At that same moment, sitting on a queen bed in a Baltimore row home, I thought I was an alien and Jennifer Love Hewitt was my mate, and I thought that Tim Burton was also an alien. I began thinking that aliens were in charge of the world, and that I was called The One, the original alien on earth, from whence all other aliens sprung forth: I was the Adam of aliens. When Jennifer Love

Hewitt laughed, I thought she was laughing at the silly human "apes;" I was ecstatic, feeling newfound passion for my mate, the finest alien there was to offer.

At some point after this, most likely the evening of October 19, 2006, I watched *The Matrix*, believing it to be a message about the world I lived in, which I believed to be a matrix, an artificial world used as a front for reality, which was a world controlled by aliens. Fluctuating within those few days between madness and despair, I now felt the world upon my shoulders, an Atlas condemned to bear the brunt of the world's weight, never to leave his post but to see the reality of it all, that the world was just a sphere within a larger reality. I searched desperately for a way out.

With the exception of the time I drew a pentagram on paper and thought I was living in Hell, I have never experienced that level of despair before in my life; it was helplessness like no other. If I had to compare it to something, I'd say it is probably similar to the feeling a mother would get if her child were grabbed by a gun-wielding kidnapper and told if she tried to do anything he'd kill the child. In that situation, the mother may frantically search the surrounding area for a weapon or pray for a Good Samaritan to attack the kidnapper, but the possibilities would quickly pass, and as the child faded into the distance she would probably get a sick feeling in her stomach and helplessness would become a reality. Much as I felt, I imagine she'd do anything to get out of the situation.

I often felt that the world was split into two dimensions, one traveling upward and the other downward. I began theorizing that there were five dimensions: two good dimensions, two bad dimensions, and one neutral dimension. I believed WWII to be a time in a bad dimension, but not the worst dimension, and Hitler represented a very evil soul who had been nearly successful at diverting the world to the lowest dimension, which would be the equivalent to Hell. 9/11 was the second attempt of Satan – in the guise of Osama Bin Laden – to take control. Because I was in the bad—but not the worst—dimension, evil had reign, although only slightly. However, if evil gained enough power the world would be drawn downward into the lowest dimension. Living in great despair, and feeling now that Kate was destined for the good dimension and I the bad, with one Earth going up and the other down, I got the sense I would never see her again. It was as if she had died. I wept for a long time.

I studied during this time a mural by Diego Rivera entitled *Day of the Dead*, which depicts a skeletal Mariachi band, all with guitars and hats, one with a sombrero and large handlebar mustache. I took this as a sign from the *Skull and Bones* society, into which I then thought I was being initiated. As I've mentioned, one manic thought builds on another and another until they all run into an incoherent unit. The *Skull and Bones* delusion built on the stars delusion, which built on the soul hierarchy delusion, which built on the delusion about the *Divine Comedy*, which built on delusions about Nostradamus, which built on the original delusions about time. The old delusions from older manic episodes never go away, they just hibernate, waiting for a traumatic event to reawaken them.

I have not mentioned it thus far, but a recurring theme in all of my manic episodes was Plato's allegory of the cave, a portion of which is below:

[Socrates:] And now, I said, let me show in a figure how far our nature is enlightened or unenlightened: –Behold! human beings living in a underground den, which has a mouth open towards the light and reaching all along the den; here they have been from their childhood . . . and can only see before them, being prevented by the chains from turning round their heads. Above and behind them a fire is blazing at a distance, and between the fire and the prisoners there is a raised way; and you will see, if you look, a low wall built along the way, like the screen which marionette players have in front of them, over which they show the puppets.

The allegory of the cave was the original "Matrix," and I believe it influenced the writers of that movie. Plato posits that the physical world in which we immerse ourselves is an illusion and that humans are kept prisoner by their own minds, concerning themselves with mere shadows until someone or something helps them reach enlightenment, to become "released and disabused of their error."

This allegory was with me during my first manic episode and added to the notion that this world is not reality, piling upon that notion the concept that this reality can be escaped if one could only open one's eyes. During my episodes, I often waited for some tear in the fabric of reality to appear, a curtain to be pulled aside and my captors, whether aliens or the members of *Skull and Bones*, be fully revealed. The film *The Truman Show* also reminds me of this. In the movie, the main character is raised from infancy in a fabricated world designed for the purpose of creating the ultimate reality TV show, in which the protagonist does not know that his life is entirely controlled and orchestrated for television. The director of the television show makes sure that the main character is afraid to leave the small town in which he lives, ensuring that the character, Truman, never discovers that he is living in a large, convincingly real, dome surrounded by television cameras. Every other character in the small town is an actor and every action is designed around Truman. Scenarios are written and acted out for his sake.

Whether it's *The Truman Show*, *The Matrix*, or Plato's allegory of the cave, the theme of my mania remained the same: the world in which we live is not reality. This thought is a seed of madness. I say "a" seed and not "the" seed because there are many paths that lead to madness. In madness, every passageway, no matter how misguided, climbs toward salvation. But any thought, if followed far enough, can lead to madness, just as the tiniest spark can lead to a forest fire given the right scenario of dry weather and wind. The thought that this world is not reality, however, is especially dangerous because it cannot be disproven. It can be rationalized and dubbed "unlikely," but it cannot be disproven by any science, religion, philosophy, or mathematical principal. The belief in another reality – oftentimes heaven – is Gatsby's green light for all of mankind; something we hope and strive for but can never fully grasp during this lifetime.

From approximately 1 am to 3 am on October 20, 2006, I watched infomercials, receiving messages from them and, according to later recollections from my ex-girlfriend, completely checking out of reality, staring unblinking at the screen, my eyes completely withdrawn within myself as I sat, fully absorbed in the alternate reality occurring within my mind. At approximately 3 am we got into an argument. I do not recall the details, but I do recall holding up one of her green and yellow shoes (thinking it represented Rastafarianism, which is technically green, yellow, and red) and saying "Four twenty," the police number code for marijuana use. I thought she had been feeding me drugs in order to keep me from ascending to my rightful position. I yelled and left the house.

The night was quiet and it smelled cold. I walked toward my car, which was about three blocks away. The street lights at night in the city cast a wan light in the air, a sort of yellowish tint, sending shadows from the spines of small red maples that rose sporadically from the sidewalk in square plots of earth, only a few feet by a few feet. It felt surreal that the outdoors was so bright and yet not daylight, especially that evening, when I had not left the house in several days.

Convinced that the world was an illusion, the stars mere spotlights on the ceiling of a false dome, I trusted no one and nothing. I believed that all information fed to me was fabricated, as it was for Truman in *The Truman Show*. Pictures of the universe: False. Stories about history: False. Time itself: False.

That is when I made a decision that would greatly alter the course of my life.

While passing, I noticed two individuals standing in a narrow alley. Without considering the danger involved, I approached.

Since that event, I have passed this alley many times. And, often, I think nothing as I walk by. But sometimes I look down it, especially at night, and I am haunted by memories of that manic episode, seeing those two figures, dark and silent, standing in that alley, watching as I approached, my mind lost, completely malleable and vulnerable to the world.

# 15

# Whisky River

I have spoken with Jessie about the previous episode, the one in which I left the house yelling. She says she was frightened for her life. The events in this book caused me great trauma and significantly shaped my life, but they also caused trauma to those whom I love most. In some cases, I have apologized for this, but my loved ones always seem unsatisfied, as if my apology cannot take away the scar that was left behind. I feel as though I hurt them, leaving that mark and emotional trauma that may never heal. I tell myself it wasn't my fault, that I wasn't in control because of the disorder, but in reality it was my fault. One of the mottos of the Buddy Club (the club for abused children that I helped lead for my High School service project) was to be responsible for your actions, and I should be responsible for mine; not those actions associated with the mania—those cannot be helped—but the negligence leading up to the mania, my irresponsibility with managing the disorder. All I had to do was take my pills—a simple thing—but I did not. In this way, I am responsible for the pain I caused my family and my girlfriend, and I am sorry for that.

*The Matrix* fresh in my head, I thought the two men whom I approached in the alley would help me leave the phony world and enter the real one. As I walked down the dimly lit alleyway they watched intently, their faces, although young, showing no signs of sympathy for a confused soul. I nonchalantly said, "Hello," believing they were expecting me, a comfortable and relieved grin on my face—relieved to have found my saviors.

This officially begins a month down the rabbit hole, a series of events and thoughts that are so peculiar I may well have been in Wonderland.

The teenagers, probably about sixteen, looked at me suspiciously, their eyes trying to be hard but still reflecting insecurity. They asked what I wanted. I did not respond, standing with a grin on my face.

The larger of the two boys, who had a thin coat of facial hair, stepped toward me and said more loudly, "What do you want?" I did not respond and he became anxious, this time yelling, "Are you a cop?" I said I was not.

I do not recall the specifics of our conversation, but I know I followed them one block to Broadway St. in Fells Point, Baltimore, where the larger of the two entered a house. I sat on the cold white marble steps out front with the other boy, who was shorter with dark skin, a black peach fuzz mustache on his upper lip. Several minutes later the other boy returned with a girl, short and a little overweight, with long black hair and pale skin. She seemed concerned; the other two did not.

My phone rang—it was my girlfriend—and I threw it across the street, where it landed with a clattering in an alley. The smaller of the boys retrieved my phone and kept it because I did not want it back, thinking it was being used by evil forces to track my whereabouts.

Eventually the boys asked if I had a car. I said yes, and they asked where it was parked, and I walked them to the vehicle, at which time they took the keys and I climbed into the back seat. It was the first time I ever sat in the back seat of my own vehicle, and would be the last time I ever sat in that vehicle again.

They drove me immediately to an ATM and asked me to withdraw some money, which I was more than willing to do, thinking it was for a revolution which I was to head. I attempted to withdraw money but was unsuccessful. Whether this was because I didn't actually have any money or because I was not in the right mindset to enter the information properly I do not know. When I got back in the car they asked if I had any drugs in the vehicle, and I said I kept my pills under the driver's seat. These pills were Depakote, my only remaining link to sanity; perhaps the only thing that could stop my slide into madness. Uncertain what the pills were they placed them under a blue mailbox on the side of the street and the larger of the two boys drove to an unknown location. With those pills went all hope of stabilization.

In *The Divine Comedy*, the gates above Hell read "Abandon All Hope Ye Who Enter Here." Several lines prior to this statement is the stanza:

Through me you pass into the city of woe:
Through me you pass into eternal pain:
Through me among the people lost...

This was the second time I would pass Hell's gate, but not the final time. In madness, however, there is no such sign; only a gentle downward slope into a warming climate. You do not simply appear in Hell one day, you walk slowly, step by step, certain your thoughts are sane and that the warmth you feel comes from Heaven. Soon you are running, thoughts swiftly gliding through your mind, coherent to you but madness to others, and you do not notice the lights dimming or the stagnation of the air, you are too caught up in your pursuits, whatever they may be. Then the lights are gone and your own voice echoes in the darkness, returning to you different statements than you first made.

As we were driving my girlfriend called again and the smaller of the boys answered. She asked who he was and he said, laughing as he did so, that he was a drug dealer and soon handed the phone to me, but I did not want to speak with her, and after a brief, loud conversation, I hung up the phone. I don't know what happened to the phone after that; I never saw it again.

They parked my car at an apartment complex, where exactly I cannot say, but probably in Dundalk, MD, a city southeast of Baltimore, and I sat in the back seat while the larger boy went into an apartment and the other boy stayed with me. He smoked a cigarette and I asked if I could have one, having smoked only one or two cigarettes in my life, thinking at the time that I must do as much evil as possible in order to garner votes from evil people, once again thinking the process of ascension was democratic, with all individuals, no matter how evil, offering votes. As I smoked the cigarette, a Kool menthol, I do not recall speaking with the boy but I do recall feeling very cool while smoking the cigarette, my notion of coincidences completely gone, thinking the word "Kool" was intended for me—a sort of pat on the back from the cigarette companies as I made my ascension.

Any concept of time was gone; any concept of reality was gone; any concept of self was gone. I was a formless being floating in a world that I believed was created for me. I was essentially thinking like an infant.

About this time I began thinking I was one of the four horsemen of the apocalypse, Death specifically, and my absorption of cancer-causing smoke was a way of capturing the power of Cancer, which was an all-time killer and would significantly increase my strength.

I realize that very little of this makes sense, but to read these things is to experience my thoughts at the time, to step into the shoes of a manic individual and truly understand what it is like. From the outside, these thoughts seem mad, but they were absolutely true to me, as true as the fact that the sun will rise tomorrow.

Eventually, the larger of the two boys returned and we began driving again. The smaller boy rummaged through my CDs, and at my suggestion put on *Renegades*, an album by Rage Against the Machine. He turned the music up and the three of us—two misguided teens and one manic person who thought he was Death—drove down the street toward yet another unknown location, the bass thudding in our eardrums.

G.H. Francis

We drove down a small road behind some townhouses, many of the houses with green chain-link fenced yards, and stopped behind one. I remember a metal tool shed in one backyard. Another boy, a tall Caucasian with a shaved head and approximately eighteen, and a blond-haired girl of about the same age got in the vehicle. The boy, whom I assumed to be the leader of the group, was wearing a black jacket with white skulls on it, which I took as a sign of his allegiance to me, Death. They asked what I wanted to do and I said, "Everything bad." They were thrilled to no end by this response.

As we were about to make a left turn at a light there was a loud pop. I asked what had happened and the leader made a gun with his hand and mock-fired, his hand kicking backward from the imagined force. The driver pulled into a parking lot and we all got out of the vehicle. One of the tires had blown. They asked if I had a spare, but I don't think I responded—I just stood there, silent, motionless, and watched, thinking they were my servants. I was also thinking about the deceased rapper, Tupac Shakur, although I cannot say in what context, and as the eastern sky began to brighten, the dark of evening becoming navy blue, the blue changing to lighter hues with each moment, I was certain I was in a *Grand Theft Auto* video game. After rummaging through the miscellaneous items I had in my trunk, items I would not see again until over a month later (a green and brown plaid shirt, a sleeping bag which was later stolen, and some other random items), somewhat confused by the oddness of my camping gear, they found the jack and the spare tire. They asked if I knew how to change the tire but I did not respond, so they enlisted the help of a man, possibly homeless, who was sitting on the stoop of the bar at which we stopped. The bar, Whisky River, was precisely 3.9 miles from where I was initially taken in the car.

The sun had almost fully risen by the time the man fixed the tire. We drove on. We stopped at another townhouse, and they told me to go inside. I did, and there was an older, overweight, witch-looking woman inside with shaggy hair and missing teeth. She told me to go upstairs to bed, but I heard a ticking noise, probably a kitchen clock, and thought it was a bomb. Thinking it a trap, I left and went back out to the car, where the teenagers were still waiting. I got back in and the leader pulled out a blunt, which he lit and offered to me. Again believing I needed to take in as much evil as possible, I took several huge hits, coughing after one of them, much to the amusement of the teenagers.

They drove to a 7-11 and parked across the street. The leader said, "We'll be back, Cool G." I was very honored by this title, and I sat patiently in the car waiting for them while staring at the water spots on the rear window and thinking that I was God, that the spots were stars representing all the souls beneath me. They returned and I soon fell asleep.

# 16

# Zeus, the Goat Pelt, and the CIA

When I awoke I was alone in the backseat of my car. The windows were down and it was late morning or early afternoon. The car was in front of a small house near a brick church. I did not see the keys, and I had no cell phone, and I was not in my right mind, so I began walking and found a path behind the church, which I followed thinking I was once again Mercury and had a message for Zeus. As I walked I passed, and I swear this is what I saw, the skinned hide of a goat laying in the center of the trail. Thinking this was a clear threat from Satan, I began to run. I reached the far side of the trail, which opened up to a small park, with a road beyond. Parked on the side of the road was a white van, which I believed to belong to the CIA, which was monitoring me.

The elation of mania was always counterbalanced with the fear of paranoia, the two oftentimes intermingling and entwining. One moment I was God, the next I was hunted by Satan, the CIA acting as his minions. I suppose we have all experienced paranoia at some point, the feeling that people are looking at you because you have a stain on your shirt or something in your teeth, but clinical paranoia is something else entirely. You can't get out of a crowd and escape it, can't go to the safety of your own home, because your home is being watched by the CIA and the television is sending you signals to control your brain. You can't get away, no matter how many rational thoughts you tell yourself.

While I was dating Kelly between my first and second manic episodes I had a psychiatrist who allowed me to control the sessions. He waited for me to talk, and I did, but the conversation soon ran out of steam and we began discussing movies or some other inane topic. I always left the sessions feeling more paranoid than when I entered them, as he attempted to rationalize my paranoia by saying things like: "Do you think the CIA is monitoring you now? Do you think they have a bug in this plant here? So what if they do." Instead of taking this goading as reasoning, most of the time I believed that there was in fact a bug in the plant and that my psychiatrist was working in collusion with the CIA. As is apparent in this book, paranoid and manic themes recur again and again, as though they are stored in a portion of the brain only accessed during mania.

Dehydrated, hungry, and confused I ran in the opposite direction, again passing the goat pelt, until I was at the car. I started walking and continued beyond the car, hearing a radio in someone's house. It seemed to me that the voice on the radio was old-timey, as if from the sixties, with that Ed Sullivan inflection, like one of those guys who calls horse races. In fact, I thought I *was* in the sixties, believing I was going through the face of John F. Kennedy Jr., who had been assassinated in 1963 and was therefore a higher ranking in the hierarchy of souls. It didn't help that the neighborhood I was in was probably built in the fifties or sixties, some of the houses having characteristic metal awnings.

I continued walking until I came to a baseball diamond, passing a group of kids on the way, one or two riding bicycles that were too small for them. Sitting on a green bench usually reserved for baseball players, I looked down on the ground at a clump of leaves and sticks. At this point I was God, or at least a demi-god, looking down on the universe, which was represented by that clump of leaves and sticks. In that clump I saw a cross, representing Jesus, and a rabbit, representing Easter, and a Jack-o-lantern, representing Halloween. The holidays, you see, also divided power among them, with Easter representing religious power and Halloween representing the power to frighten people. Terror was a very strong market. I sat there for at least fifteen minutes (although time was irrelevant at this point) and moved, added, or removed sticks to the clump, thinking I was reestablishing the proper order of things.

Eventually, I got up and began walking again. Across the street I saw an older man, probably in his sixties, with black hair, pants pulled up high on his stomach, and a crew cut. He could very well have been from the fifties or sixties, and this certainly did not help my delusion. I crossed the street and stood in front of him, thinking he was my dead grandfather. With a large smile on my face, I shook his hand, much to his befuddlement, and said it was nice to meet him. I was overwhelmed with joy, having finally met my grandfather.

I continued down the street and saw a bright yellow Mustang, freshly washed and beading with water, a bucket of suds and a squeegee behind it. Thinking I was in a game show and had won the car, I walked to the passenger door and attempted to open it, but it was locked, so I continued walking.

Two blocks later, as I was about to cross the street, a large grey pickup truck pulled in front of me and lurched to a stop. A large, bull-like man slammed the door violently and rushed around the front of the vehicle, shouting, "You messing with my girlfriend?" I said I didn't know what he was talking about, and, seeing he was about to charge, put my fists up to my cheeks, as boxers do and as I was trained to do. He throttled towards me, but I do not remember that moment; it went too quickly. Suddenly I was on all fours and pinned against a chain link fence with his knee on my neck. The woman whose fence I was pinned to came outside and spoke with my assailant, and several minutes later a police car pulled up.

I was handcuffed with plastic, white zip ties and placed in the backseat of the police car with another individual, a middle-eastern looking man in his early twenties who had dark eyes and some facial hair. I remember that he was wearing grey sweatpants. I believed the man represented Osama Bin Laden, the King of Terror. I, being Jesus and representing the exact opposite principals, was his brother, and together we'd tried to usurp God's power by bookending the power structure, he taking the low road and I taking the high road. I said, "I guess we'll have to do it differently next time."

I now see humor in this situation, as, upon hearing this statement, the officer no doubt thought that I was in cahoots with this man, most likely linking whatever he did with whatever I did, which, as far as I could tell, was nothing. I was charged with first degree assault for punching my assailant, which I may or may not have done; however, if I did punch him, it was in self defense.

# 17

# Central Booking

A t Central Booking in Baltimore City, I was seated on a bench with approximately four other individuals, directly across from a bench with five individuals on it. Completely oblivious to my situation, I nonchalantly slipped one of my hands out of my zip ties, brought my hands—which had been behind my back—to the front of my body and slipped my hand back into the zip ties, the excess plastic from the tie pointing upward like bunny ears. I thought they represented bunny ears on a television, giving me the power associated with one of the most influential items in human existence: TV. Across from me, a young man also struggled to slip out of his zip tie but was unsuccessful.

A guard at the heavy metal door through which I had entered waited at one end of the room. He was African American and heavyset, and I thought he was Martin Luther King, Jr., believing at the time that I was in some sort of dimensional holding area where powerful souls could be found.

I was then taken to a window with metal bars on it and an open slot at the bottom where papers could be passed back and forth. I was handcuffed—this time with metal handcuffs—to the window and asked by a woman behind the bars to fill out some paperwork, which I did. I have no idea what the paperwork was, but I recall thinking that passing the paper back and forth was part of some elaborate ploy to sneak me into Heaven.

I was then taken to a room and seated on another bench with five others. One of them had a tribal tattoo on his arm that I kept staring at. Here I waited until my picture was taken and I was fingerprinted. Believing the flash from the picture had made me invisible, I tiptoed softly out of the room and into the original holding area, where I crept up to the large metal door and attempted to open it. The man whom I believed to be Martin Luther King, Jr. laughed a little and took me back into the other room.

To the outsider, I must have seemed drugged out of my mind—just another druggie at Central Booking. I was taken to a holding cell.

The holding cell was not large and must have had twenty people in it. One man, a big African American with a shaved head, was wearing a LaDanian Tomlinson San Diego Chargers jersey that was powder blue with yellow lightning bolts on the shoulders. I thought he was Thor, Norse god of thunder. Another Caucasian man was standing insecurely in the corner, wearing a sweater and seeming out of place. I pegged him for a pedophile. He had red eyes and I thought he represented the Red Dragon (either a reference to the Slifer the Dragon card in *Yu-gi-oh*—one of the most powerful cards—or the Red

Weapon in *Final Fantasy VII*, which is one of my favorite video games, both representing to me the dragon from the Book of Revelations). For some reason I believed that the Red Dragon man represented Bill Gates, a very powerful soul. There was a young man, probably eighteen, lying on his stomach on the floor with his head resting on his elbow. I shook him, trying to get him up, and was told by the others I was going to get my ass kicked if I didn't stop.

After what must have been an hour I was taken to a very small room with a large glass window with a slot at the bottom. The area behind the window was very bright and seemed like some sort of office, with an occasional person walking across my field of vision. I was asked to fill out some paperwork, again being completely oblivious as to the purpose of this paperwork, and then I sat for a long time waiting for the clerical worker to return, passing the time by looking at the graffiti-covered green walls. I looked at the signatures on the wall, believing they were votes for me or words of encouragement as I ascended.

After awhile I was taken to another private holding cell, this time a narrow cell with a small glass window. Across from the cell was a cinderblock wall that had been painted white, so I could see the divots and lines where the mortar was joining the blocks. I believed at the time that I was number Ten, the tenth in a line of very powerful souls, the final soul whom everyone had been waiting for, the one needed to lift the world into a better dimension.

Where these thoughts came from I cannot say, as there were no symbols for ten or X's anywhere in my line of site. During my first manic episode, I did draw an X on the compendium of

G.H. FRANCIS

saints that I carried with me when I visited Father Jeromy. Looking back, it seems as though I had reached the same level of mania as the first episode, and in doing so unlocked a gate that had long been closed. The knowledge that these things are still within me, dormant, but waiting, keeps me humbled by the disorder, knowing that any lapse in responsibility can easily unlock those doors once more and send me instantaneously back to those places I've worked so hard to get away from.

After another half hour I was taken to a room with a diamond design on the floor, the diamond containing smaller diamonds of different colors—blue, brown, and green. I thought the blue represented the water, the brown represented the trees, and the green represented Robin Hood, whom I now suddenly became.

During my brief stint as a writer for a company similar to Clif Notes, I had summarized and analyzed *The Merry Adventures of Robin Hood*. For each analysis, I was required to read the book two or three times, so I was at the time very familiar with its characters and story.

I was seated across a desk from Little John, a well-built African American man who may have been a police officer and whose first question was, "How did you get here?" My response: "I came through a wall."

I was referring to the cinderblock wall across from my recent cell, which I had associated with the album of Pink Floyd's *Darkside of the Moon*, the album cover of which depicts a solid beam of light entering a triangular prism and coming out the other side in the form of a rainbow. I believed this to mean that I could somehow pass through solid objects.

Color would also play a significant role during this manic episode, fueled greatly by Jimi Hendrix's *Bold as Love*, which associates color with different emotions. I did not subscribe to the song's particular breakdown of colors (green=envy, purple=anger, orange=youth, etc.) but the song did further my concept that colors represented specific things.

Kate once said to me that she wanted to live by looking at the world through the eyes of an alien, as though everything was completely foreign and unknown to her. That is precisely how I was then seeing the world; in my mind, I had at one point *been* an alien. Everyday things no longer made sense to me. I was parsing things to their basest form. A building, for instance, would become simply a rectangle, giving "votes" to that shape. The earth was a circle so it garnered a great amount of points for that shape. I was X, the "axis," able to split nearly any object into four equal parts. Split in half, an "X" can be a "^" and a "v," or two pyramids placed on top of one another, once again bringing to mind the pyramids of Giza.

I had studied a Diego Rivera mural called *El Hombre al Cruce*, meaning "man at the cross," which depicts a man in the middle of what appears to be four dragonfly wings. Depicted on these wings are a heavenly star in a white wispy sky, the sun and moon, and two wings which appear to show microbiological cellular elements. The dragonfly wings make an "X." For a time I believed I was Diego Riviera and that Kate was Freda Kahlo, his wife, the couple having figured out how to return to earth using their paintings.

The police officer continued to ask me questions, which I answered, and I was then taken to a room with a large inner, enclosed square, within which were nurses and clerical workers.

I waited for a while and was then taken into a side room with various types of medical equipment. I was seated in a chair and a young male nurse, who resembled a young man whom I did not like, gave me a shot. I was certain he had given me AIDs—another attempt by the forces of evil to stop me. I was very angered by this.

Even today it is almost a certainty that in any given situation I will create a nemesis. If I'm on a bus, someone a few rows back will be talking badly of me; if I'm at a baseball game, people will be talking about me and laughing. This is the schizophrenic side of my disorder, and I have learned that rational thought is the only solution for controlling the fear and anger caused by these imagined scenarios. Remember, just because something isn't real to you, doesn't mean it isn't real to me. To understand any disorder that you do not have, you must understand this. Just because something seems obviously untrue to you, does not mean I have the same thought processes. The truth of the matter is, if you were in my shoes, you'd be me, and you'd be doing and thinking exactly as I did. That understanding is the root of empathy.

I was seated at a window that opened up to the inner square of the room, which was a sort of operations center, at which point I slipped out of my metal handcuffs and threw them onto a table in the center of the square, where the male nurse was seated. The handcuffs landing with a loud clatter, the male nurse jumped back and all of those inside the square froze and turned towards me, eying me with a sort of awed annoyance. An officer approached me and asked how I slipped out of handcuffs, seeing that my wrists were scraped raw from the effort. I do not recall feeling any pain.

After this I was taken to yet another holding cell, one with a large window on the door, through which I could see all the activity in the large room with the square in the center. I stood very close to the window, feeling the warmth of my own breath coming from my nostrils as it reflected off the glass and back onto my upper lip. I watched the flurry of activity closely. There were approximately three rooms on each side of the square, and I watched nurses come and go from each, assigning meaning to their exits and entrances.

Whether or not I was hearing auditory hallucinations or actual people speaking I cannot say, but I listened intently as Jim Morrison spoke with Jimi Hendrix, although I cannot recall the details of their conversation, which most certainly pertained to me in some way.

# 18

# The Red Dragon

There were a series of loud banging noises behind the wall of the cell, attributed possibly to construction or a prisoner slamming his fists against something metal, and I recall thinking there were monks chaining a Red Dragon and hammering spikes that would hold him in place into the ground. I stood in the middle of the room, straight and in Karate stance, arms at stomach, left hand clasping right forearm, staring deeply into the distance. I stood tall with my chest out, as the next Dalai Lama should stand (I now believed I was the Dalai Lama). It was my duty to destroy the Red Dragon—Satan—who had entered into my body and was seeing everything from my eyes. If I could confuse it, the dragon would not be able to find its way back to this world.

The metal door was opened and a sandwich and juice box were placed on the floor at the front of the cell, as if I were a zoo animal and the guard, who did not want to approach me for fear of being attacked, were my keeper. Parched, I scamp- ered to the door and sipped greedily on the drink, my first liquid in approximately sixteen hours.

The benches and floor of the room were speckled with paint and the floor was black, so the specks of white paint on it looked a bit like stars in space. Taking full advantage of this illusion, I began my superhuman banishment of the Red Dragon, first by blinking, both eyes then one at a time, and closing my eyes for long periods of time then reopening them suddenly, only to close them again for another long period of time. I kneeled on the bench—splattered with varying colors of paint—and began moving my head towards and away from a single dot on which I focused. Then I moved to the floor, turning every which way—standing on my head, lying on my side, or lying face down—so as to con- fuse the Beast, eventually getting as close as a could to a single dot on the floor and staring at it for a very long time. This was the star to which I would banish the Red Dragon. I blinked one final time and stood up.

In mania, there are endless possibilities, and nothing is be- yond the realm of reality. It is like a waking dream, where every bizarre occurrence seems normal, and you think nothing about flying through space or teleporting through walls. Mania is like having your imagination become the outside world. Fantasies that you once whimsically envisioned—that you were born the Dalai Lama, that you talked with rock stars, that you were Rob- in Hood—become true. Again, reality and truth are what we make them; there is no absolute form of either, and there never will be. You can point to a blue wall and say "that is blue," refut- ing that everyone sees the same thing, but no two eyes are the same, and no two brains perceive in the same manner. There are 7 billion humans on this planet, and each of them will see a blue wall differently, not to mention how differently flies, dogs, and rats might see that wall.

Feeling relieved, I picked up my sandwich but realized I had not yet condemned Satan fully, so, deciding he should be forced to live the rest of his life as a rat, I began acting as a rat would—sniffing around, crawling on all fours, and gnawing at the sandwich, plastic bag and all. There was a piece of toilet paper on the floor with dried semen on it, and I began gnawing on that too. Believing I had to poison the Beast I walked to the toilet, which had urine in it, cupped my hands, scooped out the yellow liquid, and began sipping at it.

This was the lowest point of my life; I don't think it can get much worse than eating and drinking an unknown person's bodily fluids.

When I felt I had successfully banished the Beast to the life of a rat, I stood again in Karate stance in the middle of the room for a long period of time. Eventually, I began planning my escape. Believing I once again had the power to become invisible, I removed my clothes and placed them on the floor in the manner in which I would wear them, my long shirt sleeves slightly away from my body, with my watch and the white hospital wristband that I had slipped out of at the wrists of my empty shirt, and shoes and socks placed beneath my pants. I stood there completely naked until someone opened the door, at which time I tiptoed passed them and began creeping down the hall, believing myself invisible. Not getting very far, I was ushered back into the room and told by an officer to put my clothes back on.

I was then taken through the jail, past many cells and yelling men, to another area with small rooms branching off a narrow hallway. I was taken into a very small room and told to remove my shoelaces and belt, which I did. I was then taken to another room with a single chair and a television in it. Although the screen was fuzzy and flicking in and out of reception, I caught glimpses of the *Montel Williams Show*, so it must have been around three in the afternoon. Thinking I was John F. Kennedy, Jr. being prepared to enter Heaven, I watched television for what must have been fifteen minutes and once again attempted to sneak away through the wide-open door, making it about fifty feet down the hallway before I was called back by a large guard.

The delusion about being invisible first started when my picture had been taken. A flash went off with the camera and, poof, like a rabbit in a magician's trick I was gone. Perhaps my mind had associated flashes of light with disappearing things; perhaps I was playing off the Amish belief that cameras steal your soul. This time, I don't know what occurred to make me believe I was invisible.

I was then taken to a large cell, about fifty feet by fifty feet, with numerous cots in it. I only recall two inmates in this area, although I am certain there were others. A young, thin, African American man was huddled in the corner, looking very frightened and as though he was coming down from a drug high. He did not speak.

A rough looking Caucasian man greeted me as I entered the room; he had a scar on his shirtless chest—either from a knife wound or heart surgery—and was short and thick-built, with black hair cut close to the scalp. Instructed to strip out of my clothes, I was given a strange-looking vest and was instructed to put it on and then did so, strapping it on incorrectly so that it was sideways and my butt was half hanging out. The rough man said, "you don't want to wear it like that, they'll get you in the butt," and I eventually corrected the alignment of the black vest/apron, which was surprisingly heavy and reminded me of the lead vest you put on when getting x-rays, although longer. I was instructed to take a shower in an adjoining room.

The room was covered entirely in small cobalt blue tiles and was actually very beautiful. I thought I must be a resurrected pharaoh in a pyramid, washing the filth of three thousand years of mummification down the drain and burying my competition, Ramses II, beneath me.

When I finished my shower I was extremely confident, my chest pressed outward like a cocky teenager, and, after putting my vest back on, I stood at the metal bars at the front of the cell, yelling, "Guard, bring me some food," still thinking I was a pharaoh and believing the guard to be my servant. This request was echoed mockingly from several other cells that I could not see. Eventually I was brought an apple on a tray, which was slid into a slot in the metal bars. I ate the apple thinking I was devouring the perceived lies of the story of Adam and Eve, overcoming Christianity and thereby chaining it to my will.

Claiming one of the cots scattered throughout the room, I finally went to sleep.

I was awakened some time later, told to get dressed, placed in handcuffs and large ankle chains, and escorted down the hall in a line of other inmates. The ankle chains were so large as to be incongruous—you'd expect them to be shackled to the Incredible Hulk himself, not me and my inordinately skinny ankles. Looking back, I suspect these chains garnered me some respect, as the other inmates probably perceived me as tough and dangerous.

The line of delinquent individuals was ushered into a courtroom, my chains dragging on the ground as though I were Jacob Marley on my way to haunt Ebenezer Scrooge. We were seated on long benches that looked like church pews. The courtroom was a very large and generic-looking room, with a raised area behind which the judge was seated. A stenographer or some such individual was seated near him and there were a few lawyers on either side of the judge's bench.

Inmates were called by name and ordered to stand while their crime was stated and their bond was set by the judge. When I was called, I stood up and, as the long black-haired female lawyer was reading my crime, loudly and confidently shouted, "Hawoot." There was a moment of uncomfortable silence, all eyes turning to me, and then the lawyer continued again, at which time I again shouted, "Hawoot." I was reprimanded for this by the judge and must have had some shred of sanity within me because I did not do it again.

The word "hawoot" was derived from two things. First, it was reminiscent of a noise marines make. In fact, I believed it *was* the noise marines make. The actual sound is "OoRah" and it is used when marines are happy or in complete agreement about something, sort of like, "hell, yeah!" Somewhere deep in my psyche I had been affected by the fact that my ex-girlfriend's new boyfriend, whom she began dating a week after breaking up with me, was in the Army reserves. The second thing that the word "hawoot" was derived from is the noise an owl makes: "hoot." I believe there was a statue of an owl somewhere in the courtroom. My charge of first degree assault was read and my bail was set at eight hundred dollars.

While all of this was happening, my friends and family were in the midst of a frantic search to locate me. My older brother was contacted, and he called my parents. My sister-in-law had contacted the police the morning after Jessie had talked to my would-be kidnappers on the phone, and the police appeared at Jessie's house just a few hours before I would be arrested by a different police officer. Having last spoken to me when I was in the car with my kidnappers, and thinking they intended to harm me, my girlfriend believed that I may be dead. My family would spend the next six hours attempting to track me down, eventually discovering that I was in Central Booking, the main jail in Baltimore City.

The old Baltimore Jail is an ominous-looking building built of stone that seems to have been scarred by soot, with wide white-roofed towers at the corners and small, pointed white turrets along the walls. The jail looks like a medieval castle. So as not to confuse it with an innocuous building, the exterior bristles with shining coils of razor wire.

The prison was constructed in 1860 under the direction of architects Thomas Dixon and James Dixon. Eventually a new section of the prison was built, and this section abuts Interstate 83, which winds into the heart of Baltimore. The façade of this new section is sandy brown and spotted with tiny cell windows, through which many an inmate has gazed down upon cars passing on the interstate, no doubt thinking of Johnny Cash's "Folsom Prison," of the freedom and movement of the outside world.

I did not think of any of these things: I thought I was ascending into heaven.

CHAPTER

# 19

# Release

I was taken to yet another cell, this one with a metal-barred front and white-painted cinder block walls, and my restraints were removed. The cell was left open and I was its sole inhabitant. The ceiling was crisscrossed with pipes and was about twenty feet high and the cell itself was about fifteen feet by twenty feet, with an exposed stainless steel toilet and sink. There was a bench along one wall and I sat down on it. With the exception of a slight din from a distant cell, the area was very quiet and the hall was empty. I do not recall seeing anyone pass in the hour or so that I was in there.

Although not intending to defecate, I sat down on the toilet and covered my anus with my hand, believing evil to enter and exit from that orifice, and removed and then replaced the hand numerous times, intending to confuse any evil that may have wished to enter. I then sat bare-assed on the bench for a while before finally pulling up my pants and throwing a roll of toilet paper into the pipes on the ceiling, where it became trapped, a white tail of paper trailing down from the ceiling.

The door to my cell being open, I wandered freely in the empty halls for a while, finding nothing of interest and eventually returning to my cell. I recall hearing voices in distant cells and at one point thinking Osama Bin Laden was in one of them, hearing his voice above all the others.

Again, madness seems to store its own memories, and some of the first manic thoughts I ever had, which occurred six years earlier, concerned Nostradamus's quatrain about the return of the King of Terror, a mythical individual I associated with Osama Bin Laden after it was revealed that he was behind the attacks of 9/11.

Eventually a guard came and I found myself in another line of inmates, this time without restraints, and was ushered into the cold, black October evening, weaving with the rest of my soon-to-be-liberated inmates through a simple labyrinth of high metal fences with razor wire cuffs. We navigated the outskirts of a courtyard, waiting at a door for a while until it was opened and we were ushered into another building.

We were instructed to sit along either side of a narrow room and a light-haired young man dressed all in black whom I took for an evil Luke Skywalker was seated across from me. I remember that the areas around his eyes were as red as a raw steak. The notion of two dimensions, one going up and the other down, again crossed my mind and I felt he was the evil version of me, his appearance altered slightly because of our differing dimensions.

There was an African American officer seated behind a small desk who called inmates' names and they would, in turn, stand behind the line in front of the desk and sign some papers. When I was called, I walked to the desk and was asked to sign a sheet of paper (I have no idea what it was). I signed "XXX," believing myself to be a pirate and not intentionally being obnoxious.

When I was in my early teens, I played a video game called *Pirates* that allowed you to recruit other pirates, plunder ships, sword fight, and raid towns. Because I played this game, I felt that the souls of pirates liked me, casting their vote for my ascension and accumulating more evil votes to my name.

The officer was not amused by my signature and I was taken to a very small holding cell—the smallest yet—and once again placed in handcuffs. The walls were bare and white and the room, which was about eight feet by eight feet, was completely empty except for a single red Uno playing card on the ground. I believe it was a red 9. The room was cold because I was near the jail's exit.

After a short period of time an officer entered and my handcuffs were removed. I was then taken to the foot of a staircase guarded by a chain-link fence that went all the way up to the ceiling. You could not enter the stairwell without a key. The stairwell gate was opened and I was set free, climbing up the stairwell just as an officer climbed down, thinking we were trading places—that he was a devil entering Hell, and I was ascending to Heaven. Unbelievably, the police were now releasing me into my own custody, somehow not realizing that I was in the grips of a manic episode nor that my own family had already filed a missing-persons report.

# 20

# The Hospital

Heaven ended up being the Jail Industries Building in Baltimore, Maryland. I stood outside on the flat landing of a triangular stairwell overlooking East Madison Street, with stairs on either side of the landing on which I stood. It was dark, but I do not know what time it was. I was directly across the street from the prison's outer wall, a solid mass of black rock looming over the westbound traffic of East Madison Street. To my left, an enclosed walkway led from the prison to the industries building, the walkway looking like a miniature covered bridge, like the ones you'd find in New England: Baltimore's own "Bridge of Sighs" or "Bridge of Reliefs," depending on the direction you were walking. I must have crossed over that bridge at some point, but I don't remember it.

Two small African American children stood on the landing as well, seeming very leery of me, and I immediately asked them what they were doing. They responded, "waiting for our aunt."

Now believing that I was the resurrected soul of a Native American, I began a ritual in order to lock the evil in Hell, in the Jail Industries Building. I began gesticulating with my hands, moving my arms in circles, pressing my hands outward in front of me, pressing them together, and, finally, pushing them outward behind me, one final incantation to lock the evil in for good.

This particular delusion was probably derived from Jim Morison's story about the dead Indians on the highway, several of which he believed to have jumped into his soul. I had already had an auditory hallucination about Morison, so it was not out of the question that this story was on my mind.

By this time, an overweight African American female guard was standing behind me, no doubt concerned for the safety of the two children, although I do not recall having heard her say anything. I walked down the short outer staircase and headed west, making my first left on Constitution Street and descending downhill towards East Monument Street, which I crossed, continuing on Constitution. There was a long brick wall on the left-hand side of the street and a large fenced-in parking lot on the right.

One would think that the ordeal would be over, having successfully escaped Hell, but there is always something else to keep the manic mind wandering—a little carrot of madness dangling just out of your grasp that keeps you walking or running into the great, crazy unknown.

I stopped by a parked police car and leaned against the hood. After a moment, I noticed a small brown paper bag on the street and found a glazed donut inside. Thinking this a gift from the gods, a way of "devouring" my jailers, of subjugating all of law enforcement to my will, I devoured it hastily. A cockroach scuttled across the road and I ran to him and stomped, smashing the thumb-sized insect beneath my brown Saucony running shoes. I don't believe my shoelaces were ever returned, so the tongues of my shoes flopped around like bunny ears. I picked up the squished cockroach, held it to my head, and inserted it in the brown paper bag, which I closed and placed exactly where I had found it, grinning at the thought of the donut-owner's surprised face when they found a squashed cockroach instead of their precious treat.

Being born between June 22nd and July 21st, I am a Cancer— the crab. Being a resident of Baltimore, the crab capital of the world, AND being a Cancer, there was now no doubt in my mind that I *was* a crab. So, naturally, I began walking sideways on Constitution Street, my fingers acting as pinchers, and being careful not to stare with both eyes at the street lights in the gated parking lot, which belonged to the Red Dragon. Try to imagine a wild-haired, sleep-deprived, just-released inmate shuffling sideways down a street, his hands raised and pinching the air, his eyes alternately blinking: that was me.

Soon abandoning my crab-state, I walked up the slight hill leading back to Madison Street and was followed by a group of prison guards, whom I turned and faced, walking backwards. I stopped at a street light and stared at it intently, it being the eye of the Red Dragon, complete with pupil, iris, and eyelid (this is the one time I may have had a visual hallucination), and was suddenly grabbed by my brother and father, who attempted to pull me away. I struggled, refusing to turn away from the light until I placed my hands close to my head so that they were on either side of the light, and closed them, covering the light completely with my connected hands. My work done and the dragon defeated, I followed my brother and father to their car. My family had arrived at Central Booking just after I had been released. It is miraculous that they found me on the street before I did any real harm, and I am greatly thankful they did.

A medium-sized bottle of orange Gatorade was waiting for me in the car and I gulped it down greedily, having drunk little in the past day. I remember relatively little from the twenty-five minute drive from Baltimore to Towson, only that I believed I was the Dalai Lama, and, having successfully conquered the Red Dragon, that I was in high spirits.

When we reached the hospital in Towson we were seated in the ER waiting room. A television was playing and I walked up to it and turned it off and my brother, speaking to me as if I were a child, instructed me to turn it back on. I did and sat back down.

Two young men who couldn't have been older than twenty were seated across from me. Looking intoxicated or high, with dark bags under their eyes and disheveled hair, I assumed they were evil. I turned to one of them and said, proudly and confidently, "What's *your* problem?" My brother once again spoke to me as though I were a child, telling me, "no, don't say that," and such things. For all intents and purposes I was a child, a prisoner to my own whims and unable to control my wildest impulses.

I was eventually escorted down a hall, this time looking at the floor and not the ceiling, watching the watery reflections of the lights on the polished white tiles, dodging the diamond-shaped designs in the center of the hallway, once again believing, as I did in the jail, that they represented the elements.

Placed in yet another solitary room, this one all white with a camera in the corner of the ceiling, I was provided with a blue, plastic-covered mattress and given some Geodon (I distinctly remember the nurses saying the word "Geodon" because the word contains letters from my name as well as the word "don," my high school mascot) and some disk-shaped yellow pills. Geodon, the brand name for Ziprasidone, is used to treat symptoms of schizophrenia or mania in people suffering from bipolar disorder.

I swallowed the pills willingly and was locked in the room, which had a small window through which I could see another very small room connected to a private bathroom and beyond that the door to a busy hospital hallway, down and across which nurses and doctors constantly walked. I was soon given food and placed the empty tray and drink cartons under the head of the blue mattress, intending to bury the very physical necessity of eating. I again believed I was a resurrected pharaoh, and I spent a great deal of time studying the lines on the floor, believing different sized sections to represent my inheritance.

Recently, I found myself in a discussion about megalomania, which I mistakenly assumed was an unquenchable thirst for power. Although that is an aspect of megalomania, the term refers to a state in which a person has an inflated self esteem and there is an overestimation of their powers and beliefs. Not found in the Diagnostic and Statistical Manual of Mental Disorders (DSM), megalomania, an old term, is most associated with narcissistic personality disorder, which has attributes commonly found in manic individuals.

The goulash of mental dysfunction experienced during mania is so expansive that the term mania is used as an umbrella term, described as "a state of abnormally elevated or irritable mood, arousal, and/or energy levels." In itself, mania is not a mental disorder. I think of it this way: The mind is a skyscraper, with the lower floors representing depressed disorders, the middle floors representing the normal range of emotions, and the upper floors representing psychotic disorders. You can take the elevator to any floor and get off. On any floor you can look at photographs you keep on the walls from previous experiences on that floor, and, like most skyscraper office buildings, you can wander to different departments, which, in the human mind, are emotions: anger, fear, love, happiness, etc., all with their own pictures. As you climb higher, you enter the psychotic disorders, so your perception of love from that height is not simply that you a woman makes your heart flutter, it is that that woman is Beatrice from *The Divine Comedy*. Fear is not simply a dislike of snakes, as may be normal; it is a belief that the devil is sending police to stop you from ascending to your rightful position in heaven. The emotions are the same, but the stakes increase as you climb, as do the physiological responses. When you near the top, happiness is the belief that you are a pharaoh, and anger is the thought that you will crush Ramses II for giving the Sphinx the body of a lion. If you have never been to those floors before, you will snap pictures of everything you see and start throwing them into departments, so that eventually pictures are strewn everywhere and, in mania, you are running around without direction, wildly snapping pictures of anything you see, or scrambling through the photographs on the ground and connecting each with the next one you pick up.

It is impossible to say if the emotion comes before the picture association—if you feel happy, go to that department, and pick up the nearest picture—or if you look at a picture and associate an emotion with it. I suppose it does not matter. The nurses had given me pills that would hopefully put me back on the elevator and take me down a few floors.

I became extremely tired, probably due to one of the pills I had taken, and the thought came to me that if I went to sleep I would be killed, but I lay down anyway. I remember the artificial scent of that plastic mattress and how I nearly fell asleep. Abruptly, I stood and, zombie-like, dragged myself to the door with all the strength I could muster. Facing the door, I did a handstand so my feet were leaning against the door, my hospital gown falling over my head and my genitals exposed to anyone passing in the hall. I believe I was attempting to reenact the reversal of Leonardo Da Vinci's *Vitruvian Man* drawing, the famous circular diagram of a man with outstretched limbs that is often used to portray human anatomy. I righted myself and, believing it was necessary for me to evacuate all of my bodily fluids on the door, I urinated, ejaculated, and spit upon it. I then relieved my bowels on the floor and, seeing a disk-shaped yellow pill in my feces, picked it up and ate it as though it were a Spree candy.

In the aftermath of mania, as you try to process all of the insane actions you performed, it is difficult to convince yourself that you can ever truly be sane. Over and over, you tell your-self that it wasn't the real you that did these things, it was the mental illness. Then you're stuck wondering where the "real you" ends and the mental illness begins, stuck wondering when you lost control, stuck wondering if the "real you" even exists anymore. And then you return to the age-old question: "Who am I?" Surely you are not the mad person who did all these acts, but you were that person for a few weeks, and so what happened to the "real you" when the "mad you" took over? Such questions would boggle even the most rational, level-headed person.

After the nurse came in and cleaned up my mess, they left the door unlocked so I now had access to the adjoining small room and bathroom. The door to the hall had a very small window, like a porthole, and I stared through that at the ac-tivity in the hall, especially noticing the lights: two small red sensors at the foot of the doors leading to the hallway and four bright lights in the distant parking lot, two on each side of a large smokestack. I could see into the parking lot be-cause there was a large glass doorway with sliding doors, through which patients from ambulances would be hectically ushered into the hospital. My small window had a yellow dot on it, from what I cannot say, and I took it upon myself to cover up the lights with this dot, closing one of my eyes so I could better focus on it. When one of the red sensors would go on, I quickly moved my head and changed my perspective so the yellow dot covered the light, believing this process was wiping out the evil that was represented by the red lights.

I did this for what must have been hours because after a while it turned light outside. On October 21, 2006 the sun rose at 7:24 am. Feeling as though my vigilance had allowed the light to return, my job was completed and I permitted myself to sleep.

It could have ended there, but the Fates chose a different destiny for me.

# 21

# Reinstitutionalized

When I awoke I was in the Springfield state mental hospital. I do not know how I got there, nor do I recall the initial check-in process. In my memory, I just woke up there one day, which would have been some time in the afternoon on October 21, 2006.

To those who have never been in one, a mental hospital is the most interesting of institutions; the apathy, depression, and mania of the patients fill the environment like an oppressive mixture of smog, tears, and flowery perfume. Even the employees seem affected by the ethos, acting alternatively numbed by the ceaseless tide of moods, or as overly-enthusiastic as preschool teachers talking to four-year-olds. Above all, there is a pervasive sense of distrust: the patients don't trust the staff, the staff doesn't trust the patients, and the patients don't trust the other patients. For a patient suffering from paranoia, as I was, the hospital took on a wartime feeling, and I was constantly on the lookout for spies or questionable individuals acting out against the imaginary republic I'd created in my mind. For me, a mental hospital was as chaotic and incoherent as a painting by Heironymous Bosch, the early sixteenth century painter who often depicted demons and bizarre creatures, such as fish with legs, in paintings such as *The Garden of Earthly Delights*.

Here is a brief roster of my fellow patients (these names, like all others in this book, have been changed):

*Hershel*: A tall, skinny African American man with thick black-rimmed glasses which I thought to be fake, who liked talking about the Navy. He also wore one of those Navy ball caps with a picture of a ship and its name on it.

*Lucinda*: A weathered African American woman with a lazy eye who often rambled incoherently and alternated between wearing red and blond wigs.

*Chase*: A short Caucasian man with a Vandyke (goatee and mustache), short salt-and-pepper hair, and a cocky strut and attitude who seemed amused by the inhabitants of the hospital. He was one of the more sane patients and always wore a grey sweatshirt.

*Darnel*: A big, young African American man, probably around twenty-one, who was about six foot three and two hundred and fifty pounds.

*Betty*: An overweight African American woman with large, clear glasses and an innocent, frightened demeanor.

*Sheila*: An older Caucasian woman with a life-worn face and a missing tooth. She was very spirited and crass, the kind of woman you'd expect to be homeless.

*Neil*: A muscular, tattoo-covered, long-haired, mustachioed White supremacist.

*Vince*: A short, thin, tough Italian-looking man in his fifties who spoke as though he were straight out of *The Godfather*.

*Mike*: A quiet African American man in his thirties who seemed to know what was going on at all times.

*John*: A long, brown-haired, long-bearded, tall Caucasian who grunted and mumbled rather than talked. He looked like a recluse you'd expect to find in the middle of the Alaskan wilderness.

*Damien*: A well-built African American with the personality of a football player.

*Lionel*: An obese African American man who was religious and spoke as though he had phlegm in the back of his throat.

Those are just a few of my fellow inhabitants at the Springfield state mental hospital. As I was there for twenty-six days, many people would come and go during that time.

Let me describe the layout of my new "home." The main area was shaped like a U, with the entrance door—always locked—at the tip of the right arm of the "U" and the middle space of the letter representing the staff area, from whence the pills were handed out at a window near the door. There was a large glass-paneled window looking out from the staff area onto the common area (at the bottom of the U") which reminded me of a doctor's office, complete with sliding glass panels. The bottom, arched section of the "U" was the large common area, in which several tables and about five large, blocky wooden chairs with plastic plaid cushions were arranged in front of a television. There were a few tables against the walls on either side and the patients' rooms opened onto this area as well. My room was located on the bottom, right-hand side of the "U." In the common room and situated at the very bottom of the "U" was a large glass window that opened up to a small, fenced-in patio. Near the bathrooms in the left tip of the "U," there was a hallway with doors to various administrative offices. A row of windows on the other side of the hallway overlooked a large, grassy courtyard. There was another locked exit door at the end of this hall.

The unit was always warm and didn't have a particular odor, although I do remember the strong smell of bleach from the sheets and pillowcases.

I was housed in a room with Vince, the small but tough Italian-looking guy with a raspy voice. Our beds were separated by a sliding curtain and we each had a wardrobe, much like the one I had in the first mental hospital, with some drawers and a doored cabinet with room for hanging things.

When you have your first moment of lucidity in a mental hospital you are struck by an overwhelming sense of loneliness; you do not know these people; you don't even know who *you* are. I sat on the corner of my small bed, about the same size as the bed in the first mental hospital, with metal springs that squeaked when you sat on it and a thin plastic covered mattress, and stared into space. I was not frightened because I was not yet of sound mind, but that moment of clarity will stay with me forever, and in that moment I may have questioned the reality I had been living for the past week, the reality in which I had been, alternately, an alien, God, a horseman of the apocalypse, Mercury, a pharaoh, etc. Reality, for me, was ever-shifting.

I have since asked, "what is reality?" and I believe that reality is what we make it. There is no such thing as a true reality because everyone has created their own reality, in which they are the star of the show. No two realities are the same and therefore the notion of "reality" is just that: a notion. It is similar to the concept of "beauty," which is different for each of us.

Aristotle spoke of forms. Forms are the subconscious ideals that we hold for all things. If, for instance, you are going shoe shopping, without knowing it you have the "form" of a perfect shoe within your mind, and when you buy your new shoes you've done so because they've most closely matched the ones you purchased to the form in your mind. No shoes could meet the form exactly, but you settle for something similar. What we consider beautiful is that which most closely resembles our forms.

Reality is also a form. Within our mind we each have constructed our own notion of the ideal reality, placing ourselves somewhere within it, most likely in a position of importance. It is true that there is an accepted bubble of reality—culture—which most of us believe to be the norm, attributing all things outside the cultural bubble as "weird." The more individuals and cultures you draw into the bubble, the larger it gets and the more blurred the bubble's edges become: one becomes more open and accepting. In the

Catholic religion, it is considered normal to believe there is an old bearded man in the sky controlling everything. In Hinduism, Vishnu is a many-armed god with great power. In Scientology, we are descended from aliens. When one exists within the structures of these religions, these beliefs seem entirely sane, as my beliefs seemed sane to me inside the bubble of my mania. These beliefs, true or not, define our personal realities. Atheists have their own cultural bubbles—they are inescapable, even if some bubbles are bigger and more flexible than others. Taken to the extreme, we all exist within the structure or bubble of our own universe, which seems sane to us, but for all we know our universe exists inside of a marble that is being used in a game of marbles played by aliens, as is the case in the film *Men in Black*. Of course this is improbable but the point is, from within a structure, a thing seems sane and feels like reality, but when viewed from the outside that reality seems absurd. Reality can only be defined when you have the full picture, and we will never have the full picture, so a universal reality will never exist. In the end, I believe if it is real to us, then it is our reality, and that is the only reality that matters.

My reality at the time was that I was a patient in a mental institute, and this reality soon became populated with witches, Indians, and dead rock stars.

# 22

# Springfield

I knew nothing of what was occurring in the outside world. All I knew was that I was supposed to line up at the window when they called "medication!" and wait for them to dispense my little paper cup of pills and my Dixie cup of water. I also knew that at breakfast time we all lined up against the wall near the door and were then herded down the hall like zombified cattle to a cafeteria area, where we huddled near another sliding window waiting for our names to be called.

I had requested that I not receive eggs or milk because I believed it was unholy to eat eggs. I had become preoccupied with food altogether, believing that each item gave me different powers and that everything I ate represented someone who had attempted to hinder my ascension. Oftentimes, I felt my oatmeal was poisoned and I would not eat it; although I did not reveal this belief to anyone.

Always an outcast, I didn't fit in with any of the social cliques in the ward and I kept to myself. My first day there, my parents brought me a bag of clothes and some books. The bag of clothes included a Guinness-logo shirt and boxers which—Kate being Irish—I believed were symbols of her support for me during this difficult time.

Guilt has a way of manifesting itself during manic times and, although it had happened at least a year prior to my hospitalization, my guilt about telling Kate I loved her while I was still dating Kelly still hung heavy on my soul. Two young women worked at the hospital, one taller and blond haired, the other short and black haired. They looked similar to Kelly and Kate respectively, and I was certain they were agents of the women I had loved.

I believe that I have a certain understanding of prison life now. If you are strong, you are feared. If you demonstrate some sort of skill, you are respected. I am a decent chess player and was able to beat everyone in the ward with the exception of Darnel, the young African American man who beat anyone without difficulty. He was clearly familiar with the game and was highly intelligent, yet drove a truck for a living.

My second evening there I heard Vince, my roommate, masturbating in his bed. I cannot say that I was affected one way or the other by the situation: it was just another odd thing that was happening to me in a long series of odd things. I was not disgusted, angry, or fearful; I was indifferent.

Here's the daily routine: In the early morning I am woken by a knock on the door and expected to walk to the bathroom to brush my teeth. A staff member standing watch at the door, we patients brush our teeth together two at a time, one resident at each of the two sinks. Occasionally a line forms behind the sink and I watch, in the mirror, the grimacing faces of the others brushing, either vigorously, baring their frothing teeth as though fending off an attacker, or lackadaisically, barely whisking the plastic bristles across grimy incisors stained from poor hygiene and difficult years. Most patients are doped and groggy in the morning and few people speak when we get lined up against the wall for breakfast, facing outward towards staff and anxiously awaiting our go-ahead.

We were then directed to the cafeteria, which was medium-sized with large glass panes on one side that looked out into a small courtyard. After waiting for them to call my name, always mispronouncing it, I generally sat by myself at the window, staring out onto the grass as though each blade represented a memory from my former life.

This hospitalization was in many ways more traumatic than the first. Not only because of the events that led up to it—the kidnapping/joyride, the prison, the hospital—but because this time I could not shrug the hospitalization off as a one-time thing, a fluke that was the result of a bit too much alcohol or marijuana. I was, for the second time, a patient in a mental hospital. This meant that the mental disorder was forever, not just something I could get rid of by popping a few pills.

For the first few days I did not participate in group activities, instead opting to sit in my room and read; although I was forced to leave my room daily, which was in turn locked behind me in order to prevent my reentry.

During my first few days I discovered a yellow Uno card in one of the glass display cases, slipped there as though intended to be found. Recalling the red Uno card I had seen in one of the prison holding areas, I took it as a message, a "we're watching you" from the police. The paranoia and mania were still with me.

At some point, they drew my blood and I was tested for certain ailments and diseases. The days slipped into each other; between the drugs and the monotony, it was easy to lose track of time.

The first book I read was James Hilton's *Lost Horizon*, which is about Shangri-La, a mythical, utopian valley hidden amidst the frigid peaks of the Kunlun Mountains above Tibet. The story traces the life of the hero, Hugh Conway, after a plane crash leaves him and a few others stranded in the mountains. Doomed to certain death, they instead stumble upon Shangri-La, a lush paradise where Hugh is slowly taught the ways of the lamas living there. Abandoning his outside life and committing himself to their ways, his aging slows. Still in the grips of my madness, I believed that the book had been written entirely for my purpose. I thought myself to be imprisoned and receiving messages from the outside world in the form of the book, and the idea that I might be the Dalai Lama once again crept into my mind.

There is very little to do in a mental hospital: The television is rarely turned on; a small boom box infrequently plays the collective musical choice of the nearest patients; every few hours there is a smoke break; there are board games such as Battleship and chess; and that's about it. As mentioned, I played the occasional game of chess, but I read the rest of the time. After *Lost Horizon* I read Umberto Eco's *The Island of the Day Before*, which is about a man who is stranded on a deserted ship. Although not making the connection at the time, I was very much like a man stranded on a ship, with no place to go, left alone with my own mind and no one to talk to, and trapped.

One day Sheila, an older woman with a gummy smile who reminded me of a witch, dropped her pants in the middle of the main room and started slapping her bare butt cheeks, cackling all the while as though she'd successfully cast a hex on an innocent princess. The event did not phase me in the least, as strange things happened all the time in the hospital. People mumbled, talked to inanimate objects, walked bizarrely, and gestured erratically. One day Francis, a younger African American man with a sharp face and hard eyes, stood outside on the porch and began a series of gestures, as though practicing yoga—clearly he was *not* practicing yoga. His movements were nearly the same as mine when I walked out of the prison thinking I was an Indian and needing to lock evil within the depths of hell. Perhaps he was warding off evil as well. From that point on I believed Francis was the soul of an Indian chief, most likely Sitting Bull, and that he was there to protect me. Unfortunately, Francis disappeared after about a week and I did not see him again.

Because it was late October, some of the patients were loaned blue or red jackets so they could go outside to smoke on the porch. At one point Francis wore a blue jacket and Sheila a red and I thought, naturally, that those wearing blue jackets represented good and those in red represented evil; however, I once again lost all sense of morality and began believing that the two sides were equal.

Each evening a herd of deer gathered at the bottom of the grassy hill atop which the hospital sat, where there was a narrow strip of woods. I believe it was Hershel who named the front-most pair of deer, although I have since forgotten the deers' names, and each evening when the deer gathered he would say, "there they are again, always out front." I'm fairly certain the front-most deer varied from day to day, but Hershel was excited to see them nonetheless.

Around the second week I attempted to make my escape from the hospital. It wasn't a well-thought out plan, but I figured I could squeeze through the 8-inch gap left by the iron porch gate that enclosed the entire porch area. With herculean effort I threaded my arm through the gap and attempted to squeeze my body through. The other patients supported my attempt with words of encouragement, but my stab at emancipation was nipped in the bud when staff noticed and pulled me away from the gate. I was immediately moved to a level 0.

Spring Grove Hospital uses a system of numbers to determine the stability of patients and, subsequently, the activities in which they are permitted to participate. Level 0 afforded patients no activities; they were not even allowed to leave for meals, which were instead brought directly to the ward. In order to raise one's level, it was necessary for the patient to attend groups and to act sanely.

I began attending meetings. One meeting was hosted by the blond female staffer whom I assumed to be the agent of Kelly, my ex-girlfriend. In the group we discussed activities we would do when we left the hospital. I suppose it was a means of determining whether we were prepared for real life again, and I certainly was not.

I attended another group in which we talked about our feelings. During this group Betty—the overweight African

American woman with large, clear glasses and a mousy demeanor—announced that she had tried to kill herself earlier in the day by hanging herself from her bed frame with a belt. The effort was completely useless because such a thing was entirely impossible. All the patients in the group did their best to convince Betty that her life was worth living.

One day Neil, the muscular white supremacist with tattoos and a mustache who constantly rocked back and forth, sat down next to me and began mumbling. At first I thought nothing of it, considering him as crazy as the rest of us loons, but I soon realized he was talking to me, saying things such as, "These n***ers are messing with your head, trying to control you." At first I was immune, but the comments began sinking in, and I felt the hatred sinking into me like black dye dropped into a glass of water: first separate and isolated, a single cloud of poison, then blending and mixing with every thought until the once clear liquid becomes clouded and smoggy. I walked away and these feelings soon subsided.

One day I was asked to see the doctor in order to sign some consent forms. Believing this to be some sort of trick, I pretended to be very tired, trudging to the room where the doctor, a man of Asian descent with large glasses and a round face, was waiting at a table with papers in front of him. I was certain he was working for the Chinese government, who wanted to suppress my ascension because they were the world's largest country population-wise and wanted to maintain the power associated with controlling that many souls. I sat down and lay my head on the table, groggily answering his questions and weakly grabbing the pen when he offered it to me. I thought the papers were designed to keep me in the hospital indefinitely, but I do not know what they were actually for. When asked to sign, I felt an overwhelming surge of confidence at my cleverness and I stood bolt upright and walked out of the room, satisfied that I had shown the underhanded doctor that I was onto his tricks.

Soon thereafter I watched as the two young women whom I thought to represent Kate and Kelly walked into a room together and shut the door. This room was normally locked but it was open when I tried the knob, so I entered. It was a sort of office and the two girls were at a computer, the one with black hair—who represented Kate—peering over the blonde's shoulder. They were startled and noticeably frightened by my entrance, and asked what I wanted. Believing they had a secret message from one or both of the women whom I frequently thought about, but not wanting to tell them that (again retaining some shred of sanity), I said I was supposed to meet the doctor in there. They insisted there was no doctor there and I left without incident.

Causing a stir amongst staff with this antic, I was left at level 0 for a few days until finally taken to level 1 and, after about a week, level 2, at which point I was allowed to go to the gym, where I played basketball by myself while Vince and Mike, a man in his forties with salt-and-pepper hair and frightened eyes, walked laps together around the court. I thought the two men had been sent to guard me.

When I reached level 2 I was allowed to go to the hospital library and check my email. I did so and immediately contacted Kate in order to let her know what had happened. After that I sent rather cryptic emails to my two Johns Hopkins professors, telling them that due to unfortunate circumstances I was unable to attend their classes.

I was also allowed to visit the hospital store, which was basically a free Goodwill, at which I acquired a new set of white, low-cut Converse All Star shoes and a new coat, believing that I would need these things because there was going to be an apocalypse and I was going to have to survive in a world without modern comforts.

During the final week of my hospitalization I attended a great deal of groups, including a music group in which we each chose an instrument (I believe I chose some sort of metal pipe that I struck with an accompanying stick) and played amidst a cacophony created by approximately ten mentally ill patients seated in a circle, most of whom played bongos or some sort of drum. During this group we were asked about our thoughts on time, to which I naturally responded something similar to: "because of Einstein's equation E=mc2, and because time is measured by the expenditure of energy, and because energy can neither be created nor destroyed, time does not exist." The woman leading the group gave me a rather quizzical look then wrote on the board, "Does not exist," beneath the already listed items such as "lets things grow" and "helps me remember good times." We were then given the option of listening to Bob Dylan's "The Times They are a Changin'" or Cyndi Lauper's "Time After Time". I was one of very few people who voted for Bob Dylan, and we listened to "Time After Time", the chorus of which goes talks about finding someone "time after time."

I thought this song was a message from Kate, who was letting me know that even when our souls are resurrected in new bodies we would find each other "time after time."

I had been in the institution for nearly a month and was still thinking the same thoughts that had sent me there in the first place; however, I never let on that I was thinking these things, and I was soon discharged.

My Aftercare Referral Form:

## PART I – BASIC DATA

Name of Facility: Springfield Hosp. Center
Date Admitted: 10/21/06 Release Date: 11/14/06
Conditional Release: No

## PART II – MEDICAL DATA (to be completed by the treating physician)

Reason of Admission: "NOT SLEEPING, DISAPPEARED. FOUND AT CENTRAL BOOKING AFTER ASSAULTING SOMEONE, NOT COMPLIANT WITH MEDICATION, FOUND TO BE LOUTIKING (?) INAPPOPRIATE – TELT (?) AND TALKING TO SECI (?)"

Treatment Initiated in Hospital: PHARMAOTHERAPY, MILIEU THERAPY, SUPPORTIVE THERAPY, ACTIVITY THERAPY, GROUP THERAPY

## DIAGNOSIS DISCHARGE MEDICATIONS DOSAGE SCHEDULE:

Axis I: BIPOLAR DISORDER NOS
(1) ESCITALOPRAM (LEXAPRO) 20 mg
DUE DAILY AT 9 AM
(2) VALPORIC ACID 500mg PO BID

Axis II: NONE

28 DAY SUPPLY GIVEN WHEN DISCHARGED

Axis III: HIG HYPERLIPIDEMID

Axis IV: NONCOMPLIANT

Therapeutic Drug Level: N/A

Therapeutic Range:　　　　　Date:

WITH MEDICATION

Date of last IM: N/A

Next date IM due: SALOMON B

16

Allergies & Reactions: BENADRYL

Axis V: Current: 45

Past Year: Unknown Diet: REGULAR, NO EGGS

PPD Date: 10/25/06 Results: 0 NEGATIVE.

Active somatic problems requiring continued attention: [

10/25 Labwork (52)

126478 10-21-06 N 03

1/5/M C1

A400016426


Shortly after leaving the hospital, I wrote about the experience in the concluding pages of my novel, *Lightbearer*:


After a breakdown, in the institution, you have to relearn everything. You wake up in the morning and zombie-walk to the bathroom with toothbrush and toothpaste in hand, both cheap compliments of the state or private facility. You stand in line and wait for your turn at one of the two sinks, or shower first in the timed shower and dry with the thin white towels that you need two of in order to dry off, and then you brush your teeth. The mirrors are grey and the light is pale and the patient next to you mumbles or excitedly shows their teeth to the mirror and brushes vigorously, frothy toothpaste falling from their mouth into the sink. Some days you need to shave so you let the orderly know when they ask and they retrieve your shaver from the front desk and carefully watch you to make sure you don't somehow kill yourself with a Gillette Mach 3. Afterwards you return to your room and sit on the flimsy five-inch mattress of your cot and stare into the distance, thinking where your life has gone and whether you'll ever get out of this place, and if you do get out of this place, whether you'll return to yourself or just fade into one of those crazy people who lock themselves in houses or rant and scream at street signs.

Soon they call breakfast and you line up against the wall behind the locked front door, waiting for all the patients to shuffle in position. It's always colder than it should be, and someone always gets into an argument and refuses to go to breakfast, probably because they assume the food is poisoned. When everyone is ready, an orderly opens the door and you zombie-walk down the long corridor, a silent mass of scraggly-haired, long-gazing crazy people, some of whom had been in grocery stores, made love, and laughed only days earlier, only to find their bodies herded down a corridor in a mental facility, the last place they'd ever expected to be the Tuesday after last. Outside the facility their lives were collapsing, their families were forgetting about them, their wives, husbands, and significant others were questioning whether the relationship was really worth all the effort. Oftentimes, they decided it wasn't, and another long-term patient was born.

In the small cafeteria you stand by the window and wait for your name to be called, when it is you pick up your plastic tray with French toast with apple juice, coffee, and two sliced pears in syrup, or pancakes and sausage, or cereal and milk. You sit by yourself and face the window so you can watch the squirrels hop in the dewy grass and for a moment you wonder what is going on in the world. You haven't watched the news, you've had limited contact with family or friends, you stare at your goopy oatmeal and realize this is your reality. You don't know what happened to your former life, this is the life you're living now. You're in your pajamas in a small cafeteria filled with mentally unstable individuals eating with plastic utensils and watching squirrels through a large glass window, feeling nothing at all.

After breakfast you return to your room and think about crying, or you do cry but you hide it from your roommate, whom you heard masturbating in his bed in the middle of the night.

At first you don't attend the groups because you think they're worthless and there's nothing wrong with you. After a while you realize they're going to keep you at level zero or level one, which means limited activities and, if you're level zero, no leaving the ward. So you attend the groups, participating only for the sake of increasing your level and hopefully getting access to the store, the soda machine, and the gym, where you can play basketball and get some exercise.

The days are very long and you spend them reading, and you finish numerous books but don't retain any information because you're thinking of her or the words seem to have special meaning to you...they're talking about your life and telling you secrets about the other patients. You watch some television, each female character becoming a facet of her, laughing at you or toying with you, hiding behind the television and turning your pain into comedic shows.

Patients move things for no reason and they constantly flip over cushions or cram garbage beneath them, and your books begin to disappear and turn up in strange places throughout the ward – in the drawers of desks, or on a table on the other side of the room, and sometimes you don't find the book at all and you need to start a new one. You don't ask questions or accuse anyone because this is what's supposed to be happening. The doctor is working for the Chinese and trying to trick you into signing your life away to the hospital. The other patients side with or act against you, although all are completely ignorant of their vital role in your life.

You continue to attend groups, monotonously spewing out the things they want to hear, saying, "I think it's good that you didn't kill yourself today," and "I am feeling much better today," until one day your family (if you have a family) shows up at the door and you put all your clothes in a brown grocery bag and leave the facility.

Then you're thrown back in the real world, into your old life and expected to pick up where you left off. Your family and friends laugh off the hospital stay, thinking it's like a scar that's healed and no longer needs to be dealt with. But it's not like that, you have to start all over, you have to relearn how to live.

You immediately hop back into your old life and go to the grocery store, where everybody is shuffling behind carts and removing items from shelves and placing them in carts; you are reminded of the institution and you suddenly feel that everybody is staring at you or speaking behind your back, saying you're crazy.

A few days later you return to work, but everyone is speaking about you there too, and you sit at your desk and try to convince yourself that you're normal again, but then you think of the institution, of the zombie-walkers and the racists and the garbage-hiders and you realize that you were one of them, you realize that you must be one of the crazy people. You leave work early because you are certain you are falling apart again, and you see your old, normal life falling away from you. You quit your job or get fired and spend your days watching television, when it isn't mocking you, and sleeping and crying.

If you're lucky, the state pays for counseling and medication, if you're unlucky, you wind up on the street without medication and without help.

A few months earlier you were normal.

You drop into depression, questioning your existence and the purpose of all this pain. You find yourself standing too long on cliff faces or staring at kitchen knives.

This isn't the life you wanted, you weren't supposed to have a disorder; you were supposed to be normal.

There is no beginning or logical timeline, and sanity comes only in faux stretches that become a fictional past once the threshold of madness is crossed. There are two realities, each becoming fiction in the eyes of the other and overlapping on rare occasions that I call the "cartoon existence," where life becomes a comic interpretation of Dante's Divine Comedy.

Bipolar is a difficult disease with times of great hope and euphoric thought, when ideas and focus are so keen that there is no task you cannot complete. Then there are the lows, the times of severe despair when thoughts are incoherent and fleeting, and always in the back of your mind is the shadow of suicide, a final solution to the desolation and helplessness of incurable rage. If properly medicated, there are periods of numb stability, where you are happy to be stable, but wish to be more euphoric. There are other moments (these I cannot fully explain) when one feels hope and despair in the same instant, as if your heart and mind were being pulled to every boundary of their sensations, and you just wish to end the senselessness by entering into one world or the other. All thoughts are two thoughts, the day is also the night, growth is death, sanity is madness. This duality can persist for hours at a time. This is the ultimate deconstruction of the human condition – the return to the absolute beginning, when the mind was initially split into two halves, neither of which truly exist, coming into existence as petty attempts to compartmentalize and define the inexplicable. Good and bad, right and wrong, yes and no…we learn such lessons very early in life and we never quite return to the innocence that existed prior to the great separation. The rest of our lives are ultimately divided into those two columns of good and bad, and our personalities are derived from what we've placed into each column. It is that simple.

Despite your best attempts to think clearly, you remain straddling the proverbial river Styx until new medication blocks certain chemicals in your brain from reacting with other chemicals in your brain.

Time passes and your medication and counseling begin to have an effect, and you soon find yourself at a new job with limited stress. You can't pursue high-paying jobs because you must avoid a face-paced world, and every dream you've had about the pursuit of happiness becomes a laughable fiction, one intended for normal people with brains that don't fill up with boundless hope and manic ideologies, only to again be plummeted to feelings of absolute insignificance and worthlessness. You decide, after trying to convince yourself that you can overcome this weakness, that you do have a disorder, that it won't heal, that this pain will be with you forever. Then you start over.

Your life won't be the same as it was before.

This passage would be modified, but that will come later.

# 23

# Back In the World, Again

After twenty-six days in a mental institution the real world seems large and frightening. You are no longer confined daily within a two thousand square foot space with a chain-link patio, and there are unfamiliar people everywhere, people who could be cruel and belittling, whispering taunts and accusations beneath their breath.

I was taken to my brother and sister-in-law's house, where I was to stay while I got back on my feet. My sister-in-law was pregnant and my nearly two-year-old niece ran around the house all day while I attempted to develop a website for my freelance editing and writing business.

Only slightly manic by my own standards, I focused all my time and effort on this website, spending many hours each day developing it and learning how to create a website.

I continued to write, composing the following poem:

I left my soul in many places
In photographs sealed in aging albums
In amusement parks filled with laughter
On beaches with crashing waves
In a thousand mirrors, reversed and false

I gave some of my soul to hope
And some of my soul to God
Heaps I gave to women
Who didn't seem to care

I lost some of my soul in rough bars
And much of my soul to drink

Pieces I placed in writing
With the dream they would be read
And taken, watered, and grown
Before my body's dead.

The second hospitalization left me more numb and more traumatized than the first, and in the year following I would never quite recover. I continued to drink heavily, getting to a point that I was getting drunk every day, most times by myself. *Lightbearer* was a drunken mess; it could not function as a cohesive piece of fiction, or even non-fiction, and I had to scrap the book entirely.

Despite returning to a relatively stable state, mentally speaking, I continued to have a sense that I was not in control of my own fate, that at any moment the powers that be could flip a switch and send me into madness. My fate was run by a disorder, and nothing I did could ever change that.

Although no longer dating, I continued to see Jessie, now

my ex-girlfriend, and continued to have strong feelings for Kate, who showed initial concerns about my hospitalization, concerns that a friend might have, but who knew nothing of her unintended role in any of it. As always, I confided my emotions to her through emails and was replied to with friendly but sterile responses. When in love, many of us easily convince ourselves that the object of our affection shares our feelings, projecting onto them our own emotions, and all their attempts to say otherwise are viewed as shyness or coy attempts to goad our love into action.

Still emailing Kate often, I many times sent her the titles of songs to listen to, often songs with heartfelt declarations of love in them. I did not find out until years later that she never listened to the songs, so my perception of our relationship was skewed greatly because I thought she had been receiving the messages in the songs when in reality she had not. At this time, I mentioned in an email that I would be a good person for her to marry because she loved the US and would be able to move here if she did. She responded that she had thought about it but it wasn't a good idea. This in no way affected my determination.

I began seeing a new therapist at the time but had no connection with her, and the sessions were more obligatory than anything else. I think she preferred to talk about herself than to hear about my trivial issues.

With continued work as a freelance writer and editor, I scraped by, not having to pay rent or food, electric, water, cable, etc. My life was becoming more compressed and isolated. I spent all day during the week in the house and on weekends I drove to Jessie's house in Baltimore and went to bars and partied. I was wandering aimlessly, drinking my way from one day to the next and thinking very little of the future. And then it began again.

# 24

# Number Three

It was October again. The leaves were changing, the air was cooling, and I was becoming manic.

In my experience, the first step towards re-hospitalization is sporadic pill-taking. I was still on Depakote (Valporic Acid) but, feeling good, frequently forgot to take it. Missing their pills one time will not send someone with schizoaffective disorder or bipolar into a manic episode, but for weeks I took my pills sporadically, only when I remembered to, until I was no longer in control.

Having a difficult time with thoughts of Kate—most likely due to her lack of response to an email—I drank 14 bottles of beer in about four hours one evening. When confronted, I said to my brother, "I thought you'd be proud of me." He was not proud of me.

Thus began the most confusing of my manic phases and the briefest period of time between onset and hospitalization, less than two weeks. Everything seemed to happen at once; I do, however, remember the last few days prior to my third hospitalization.

It began once again with thoughts that everything was happening for a reason, and that everything was happening for me. I recall watching a concert on television during which David Bowie sang. A recurring figure in my madness, I thought his songs were in praise of me. By the time I retired to my brother's furnished basement bedroom for the evening, which I did when his family went to sleep at around 10 every night, I thought once more that I was God and that the room itself represented the universe.

Music playing as important a role as ever, I listened to The Red Hot Chili Peppers' *Stadium Arcadium* album in its entirety several times over, focusing on a few songs, including "Don't Stop", which has the lyrics "can't stop the gods from engineering," thinking that this referenced the game in which I played a crucial role. I also focused on "Come from space…To teach you of the Pleiades." The Pleiades is a cluster of stars about 43 light years away. It is sometimes referred to as the Seven Sisters, although fourteen of the stars in the cluster are visible by the naked eye. Even so, I believed that The Red Hot Chili Peppers represented the Pleiades and that I would have to surpass them to access my rightful position in the star hierarchy.

With relatively little provocation other than the intermittent pill-taking, I had immediately fallen back into my old thoughts of a hierarchy of souls, as though there was no separation of time between my first manic episode and this, my third, manic episode. It is as though every thought from that first episode was, to once again paraphrase Bob Dylan, glowing forever in my subconscious as if seared by burning coal. I did not think these thoughts when I was not manic, and it seems like my memories were set up like a skyscraper, as mentioned before, or on climbable scaffolding, with certain memories being on certain levels, and on the highest level of scaffolding my mad memories sat, running to and fro on their platform, jumping on my back and tugging at my ears like misbehaved children, whispering devious thoughts in my ears like conspirators in a dark alleyway. When I became manic, I began climbing the scaffolding and old memories were revealed to me, level by level.

In my brother's basement there is a hanging chandelier with five bulbs at the end of five curved bronze arms. Each of these bulbs is capped with a light-brown miniature lampshade. One of the light bulbs in this light was missing, so I devised a plan to replace it.

During this manic episode in particular, I thought that the devil had the ability to see through my eyes, and I constantly attempted to mislead him, sending him in the opposite direction so that he would forever be trapped in the abyss of the past. If you remember, these thoughts also occurred during my time in the prison during my second hospitalization, when I was attempting to wipe out the Red Dragon.

To replace the light bulb, I grabbed a light bulb from the closet and returned to the basement, where I turned out the lights, closed my eyes, and felt my way in the dark to the hanging light, at which point I removed the old light bulb and replaced it with the new one. Fumbling in the dark along the wall, I regained the light switch and turned it on, once again opening my eyes after I had done so.

The purpose of this exercise was to return the Pleiades, which, in my compacted universe *was* the light, to its rightful place and therefore allow my further ascension into the heavens. I was satisfied for a moment but got the sinking feeling that the devil was still with me, so I went into the bathroom and stared at the mirror, fully aware that the image I was seeing was actually the reverse of my true self. Here, I followed a ritualistic series of motions designed to give Satan the slip: switching the light off, ducking, switching the light back on, turning around, switching the light off, turning back to face the mirror, turning the light back on, etc. Finally satisfied that I had successfully disoriented Satan, I returned to my efforts of ascension.

On the final evening prior to my re-hospitalization, I was asked to take the trash out. My brother has an end-unit townhouse, so to take the trash from the back to the front one must only walk around the side of the house; however, believing I would mislead the devil, I took the trashcan all the way around the row of townhouses, rolling the bulky can down the sidewalk behind the entire block of homes, and anyone looking out their back window should have had no question that I was insane.

Again believing I was Jim Morrison, or that Morrison was at least a very high-powered soul whom I would need to surpass—even thinking at one point that Morrison was the reincarnation of Jesus—I looked upon a small lizard made of beads that my niece had created, believing it to be a totem representing "The Lizard King," yet another vote for my ascension.

My niece had some spongy stickers in the shape of dolphins, butterflies, and dragonflies that I stuck to the table in order to create a design that had a great deal of meaning to me at the time, despite being only a mash-up of random animals. Placing two arched-back dolphins nose to nose, they roughly formed the shape of a heart, which I thought to be a sign from Kate.

After being awake for most of a week (although still sleeping a few hours each night) I went to sleep that evening at around four or five a.m. and awoke at approximately 8, at which time I climbed out the window of my basement bedroom and walked to the parking lot of my brother's townhouse, where yellow and red dots and slashes were spray-painted which, although I did not realize at the time, probably marked some sort of gas or sewer pipe beneath the ground. Following these dots around the parking lot, dodging some, stamping my foot down on others, zigzagging between them, I continued to confuse the devil. Those, if any, who observed me must surely have been latching the bolts on their front doors. With an enormous grin on my face, I knocked on the front door of my brother's house and, rather perplexed, he answered the door. He asked the standard questions you'd ask of a person who'd slept in your basement only to appear suddenly at your front door barefoot at 8 o'clock in the morning. Sensing something was amiss, he asked me to get in the car.

I remember reading the street signs on my way to the hospital and interpreting each of them as an encouraging sign, a "way to go!" message from some high-ranking soul directing me on the final leg of my journey: I was finally ascending.

It turns out I was "ascending" to Laurel Regional Hospital in Maryland. I remember the waiting room. I remember the small examination room in which I sat in with my brother while awaiting a doctor. I remember flipping the water I'd been given over on the table and forming the ice chips into a circle, representing the world (which I now ruled), and then slapping the chips off the table with my hand, dashing them against the walls and across the floor. This resulted in another thought of "it's done now," as I once again believed that the devil, which had been on that earth represented by the ice chips, was forever banished. Totally compliant after that, I was taken to a special ward of the hospital for the mentally ill.

CHAPTER

# 25

# Laurel Regional Hospital

This was the smallest of the wards I had seen as a patient. It had a small common area with a few bookshelves of board games (a staple of any mental ward) and some books and magazines, a sink and refrigerator on the far wall, and faux wood tables for eating and gathering. However, this was probably the most patient-intensive ward I ever stayed in, with frequent blood pressure and temperature checks from those portable droid-like stations with a skinny silver frame and a boxy head that displays your vitals. The nurses always recorded the results on a clipboard that was toted around in the droid's basket.

The patients in this ward were less memorable, and I recall only three vividly. One was my roommate, a young African American man who rarely spoke. Another was a young woman whose husband was in Iraq (I spoke to her once). The third was a young Caucasian man who was an artist, and whom I considered to be my alter ego from a different dimension. My goal throughout this hospitalization was to exit my current dimension and enter another, better one, which I could only do by switching places with my alter ego.

As with all other hospitalizations, I was shuffled through the daily routine: I woke up, brushed my teeth, ate breakfast, got my pills from the nurse's station, did God-knows-what for a few hours, ate lunch, did God-knows-what for a few hours, ate dinner, did God-knows-what for a few hours, and went to sleep. The in-between time was spent flipping through magazines looking for messages from Kate, stopping on any advertisement with green hills that reminded me of Ireland, reading secret codes within the text of the pages, believing each advertisement to represent either her or me, as all things were contained within the two of us. Someone had gone through these magazines with a pair of scissors and snipped out sections, so there were square holes in many of the pages. Believing that Kate had somehow snuck in there, or had someone sneak in for her, and had snipped out these sections in order to claim ownership over the magazines and thereby maintain our heavenly status, I was filled with happiness.

I remember the broccoli that smelled like feet and tasted as though it were made of plastic, I remember the potato rolls, on which I feebly attempted to spread precut pads of nearly-frozen butter, and I believe I remember having pancakes and sausage and coffee (watered down, naturally). I seem to recall sandwiches too, remembering many of the ingredients because I spent the entirety of the meals thinking about how to devour my competition, pouring sugar into my coffee (I don't like sugar in my coffee) or tea so I would have power over the sugar barons, whom I lumped with slave-owners, whom

I considered very powerful evildoers who were trying to suppress my ascension.

You may realize now that, in my mind, there would never be a final point for my ascension. When I reached a point and nothing happened, the focal point was moved a little bit farther away, until I reached it after completing some arbitrary action, at which point it was moved farther away, then farther, ad infinitum. This was, perhaps, the result of my ego protecting itself from the disillusion of my reality.

One day, the artist's brother brought some of his sketches to the ward. I asked to look at them. They were gory and suicidal, the sort of thing you'd expect to find in a misanthropic fifteen-year-old's desk drawer. Believing that the images somehow bound us to this earth, I thought I saw beyond his ruse and, after handing the pictures back to him, shook his hand, thinking I was transferring my misfortune onto him and thereby switching places, and therefore dimensions, with him.

I would repeat a similar process with my roommate, whom I passed in the hall one day and watched as he walked beyond a set of open doors, which I had determined to be the point of entry into the other dimension.

As with every mental hospital, Laurel held frequent groups, one of which was a substance abuse group that met daily. Although I insisted I didn't have a substance abuse problem, I was asked to attend the meeting, which discussed the symptoms of addiction and the standard hazards of substance abuse.

Later that evening I stole a marker from the dry erase board in the hall and snuck into the substance abuse group room, which had numerous paper printouts relevant to the topic taped to the walls.

The symbol for Alcoholics Anonymous is a triangle inside a circle. This symbol fit surprisingly well into my delusional thoughts—it containing the shape of a pyramid, and I having once been a pharaoh. Believing at this time that the pyramid represented the Illuminati, who were trying to hold me down, I gave the circle little ears, set eyes on the sides of the triangle, and drew a snout in the center, successfully turning the AA symbol into a pig.

On another piece of paper attached to the wall, perhaps one listing one of the steps of AA, I wrote a verse from The Red Hot Chili Peppers' "Snow" that refers to getting high.

This verse was surprisingly apropos for graffiti on an AA sign, although I don't think that was my intent.

The following day while attending the meeting, I looked at the graffiti and felt incredibly guilty, the well-meaning instructor, a heavyset woman with experience and pain written on her face, having not deserved the harassment. Maybe it was the guilt, or maybe the sessions were effective, but I have drank alcohol only once since that day, which was over six years ago. That was the turning point.

The third time's the charm, or so says the cliché, and I was given two options as to how the third hospitalization would affect me: I could lose all hope for myself as a human being, accepting that this mental illness would always rule me, or I could learn to rule my mental illness and accept that I am the master of my own fate. I chose the latter.

# 26

# The Smell of Leather

lthough I wrote it in 2005, prior to the final two
hospitalizations, I have always liked this poem:

Have you ever held your breath underwater
To the point where your lungs are sheets of paper
And you can't float
Cause there's no air left?
Nobody's holding you there
But you test yourself
I don't know why
We emerge
The same person
Only stronger

That is how it felt. When I was going through manic episodes it seemed as though I were drowning, out of air and
sinking deeper, flailing my limbs erratically but not knowing

which way was up. The hospitals always pointed me in the right direction, they showed which way was up, but the swim up was even more painful than the descent, because there was the feeling you wouldn't make it, that your body would give way just before you reached the air, that you'd sink lifeless to the ocean floor, lost forever within that great abyss.

Eventually, I ended the relationship with my quasi-girlfriend, Jessie, telling her outright that I was going to ask Kate to marry me. This is the actual marriage proposal email I sent to Kate. I have no record of the former emails mentioned.

Hey,

Sorry about the last emails…

I'm sober now (and plan to be so indefinitely) so I am writing this with a completely clear head and in an absolutely stable frame of mind.

Since we first met you've been the one true inspiration in my life, and I can honestly say that any accomplishment of mine has been achieved with the sole intention of impressing you. Before we met, I was a college dropout with very little motivation. That changed when we happened to cross paths as we each traveled the US in opposite directions. Since that day I have lived my life with a very single intention – to retain a lasting relationship with the most beautiful girl (woman) I've ever met. And, although our personal encounters have been relatively limited, I feel I know and can trust you more than any other person on this planet. Some may say that email is an impersonal way to know someone, I disagree. Without the fears that often hold us back in 'real' life, we can speak freely and truly get to know another person through email. Words become pure words and feelings become true feelings (a notion that I have all too often taken liberally).

If I could explain to you how these years have been then perhaps you'd understand my apparent madness. I cannot (and this is my fault entirely) look at a tree and not think about you. Thanks to our recent discussion about love, I can't even look a color and not think about you, even when I close my eyes and everything is black, I think about you. When I meet another woman, I see you in her. When I hear a song on the radio (nearly any song), I think about you. I have a disparaging feeling at all times that somehow you are always one step ahead of me and, despite the bizarre notion that you are somehow controlling me, I cannot help but follow you.

I wrote this for you several years ago...

> There are hours
> I keep for you
> In all these years
> They have been yours
> And always will be

You are the ideal woman in my eyes, and I know you will always hold that position, no matter what. You are gorgeous, smart, funny, understanding, kind, etc. You are everything I've ever wanted in a woman.

All these years have led to this... Will you marry me?

I understand if you say no and wish to end this relationship completely, but at least we it will be completed at a final point of termination, where no questions can remain.

I love you

I wanted this to be a love story; a mad tale with a happy ending. I did not hear back from her.

After months of despair and more than a few suicidal days, I had all but removed Kate from my memory, thinking of her only occasionally when hearing certain songs, such as Bob Dylan's "Tangled up on Blue" or "Simple Twist of Fate", or when anything reminded me of Ireland. A year later that simple twist of fate occurred when my Hotmail account was hacked and a spam advertisement email for erection medicine was sent out to all of my contacts, Kate included.

Much to my surprise, she sent an email asking how I was doing and the connection started all over again. My old feelings soon resurfaced and I eagerly awaited her emails each day. Distraught over a recent breakup with a long-time boyfriend of three years, whom I had never heard anything about, she seemed to be testing the waters for a potential relationship—at least that's how I perceived it. She had plans to visit her sister in New York in a few weeks, and she would visit me in Baltimore for three days, staying two nights.

I don't believe I've ever been so happy in my life, and my excitement over her visit grew with each day, until she was finally here. There was a miscommunication and I went to the wrong bus station, but when I finally picked her up she looked as beautiful as she ever had. Her hair was a little shorter, but she had not aged and her skin was milk white, her emerald eyes causing my heart to convulse icily in my chest, plucking at my rib cage like a small bird pecking at a crumb of bread. She was wearing a black leather jacket and smelled of leather, which will forever be an enduring aroma for me.

We got some food and coffee then went to a museum, touring the city the following day. I was so nervous around her that I did not speak much, although I tried my best to keep the conversation going.

On the second day, after our tour of the city, we went on a hike. Because I had forgotten my hiking shoes, I wore my old Saucony J3000s, which had seen me through two hospitalizations and which complimented her black Converse All Stars that, I believe, were made of vinyl and had been specially purchased for this occasion. I found it endearing that upon hearing we were going for a hike she decided to buy retro sneakers—Converse All Stars—the thought of hiking shoes never crossing her mind.

At one point, we sat on a log by the water, the moment playing out in my mind that this was when we'd kiss for the first time. I asked her how it was going, if there was anything between us, and, well, this is what happened:

### THE MOMENT SHE SAID NO

There are turtles in the water
Bathing in the midday sun
Their black shells
Reflecting white
The wind is calm

We are on a log
Separation between us
I smell the fresh algae
I ask her
She says no

Rubbish litters the lake shore
Grimy plastic bottles
Empty, thrown from bridges
Into the water below

I wept like a baby, standing on the shoreline with mud
squeezing up the sides of my shoes, making my J3000s even
browner than they were before. Kate hugged me as I wiped
snot from my nose. After about fifteen minutes I steeled myself and we returned to the car and went out to eat in silence
before returning to my house, where we watched a movie and
I wept, again.

That feeling is indescribable. It is the feeling of working
ten years to build a bridge to the opposite shoreline of a river
where a loved one waits, seemingly indifferent to your efforts.
Finally, you finish the bridge and begin to rush across it, your
heart aflutter. Your loved one smiles at you—a grin you mis-
take for love—lights a match, and throws it onto the wooden
boards, enflaming the bridge and separating you forever.

It is the feeling of climbing a mountain in pursuit of
someone you love, your arms shaking and flaccid, visions of
her green eyes pulling you upward until you reach the top,
standing confidently, opening your arms as the one you love
rushes toward you, shoving you off the mountainside. You
watch helplessly as the mountain face gets longer and longer
and your loved one gets smaller and smaller, until you are
back where you started.

The following day was a melancholy one and I drove her
to the bus station at "half two," which, incidentally, means
2:30 and not 1:30 as I had assumed. Both weeping, I held her

by the arms and stared into her large green eyes, greener than the lushest grass or the most vivid leaf in summer, tears streaming down both our faces, and we hugged, she grabbing me strongly until I pulled us apart. Then she walked away.

About an hour later Kate texted me while on the bus and said that she had wanted to kiss me but didn't know if she should. This was all the encouragement that my battered-but-eager heart needed. Kate had pushed me off the mountainside, but I had immediately started to climb up again. One does not abandon dreams of love so easily, despite any therapist's or friend's recommendations, and—though she never knew the half of it—I had been through too much with Kate to give up. I was heartsick and confused and when, after more months of communicating via email and Skype, she invited me to London, I was elated and wanted to believe that my ship had finally come in.

After a cancelled flight, a three-and-a-half-hour drive to Newark from Baltimore in the middle of the night, and a nearly eight-hour transatlantic flight without sleep, I finally landed at Heathrow, where Kate was to meet me at the train station. Somewhat delirious after having been awake for the better part of thirty-two hours, I became determined to kiss Kate as soon as I saw her, my feelings for her stronger than ever.

Kate must be part mongoose, because when I moved in to kiss her she turned her head with incredible swiftness and gave me the cheek. That set the tone for the three days I was in London. If our last encounter had been Kate shoving me off the mountainside, this time it felt like she stole my wallet, punched me in the face, and then shoved me off the moun-tainside. It was a horribly cold and awkward trip. I returned home, dismayed, and we continued an erratic correspondence until I began writing this manuscript. I have not heard from Kate since telling her that she is a central figure in the book. Everyone I know asks why Kate would invite me to London if she did not share the same feelings for me, and I don't really know the answer. Optimistically, I want to believe that she was too kind or too naïve to understand that I wanted to be more than a friend, despite my rather obvious expressions of my intentions. But then, I always think the best of her. It's also possible that she simply enjoyed the attention I gave her, the feeling of being loved and wanted, no matter what. The truth is—I may never know the answer.

# 27

# The Story of Icarus

The story of Icarus is well-known: in order to escape imprisonment on the island of Crete, Icarus is given wax wings and told to fly at a middle height away from the island, not so high that the sun will melt his wings and not so low that the water will splash up and weigh them down. But Icarus, feeling the exuberance of flight, climbs higher and higher until the sun melts the wax, breaking apart the wings, and he falls into the ocean and dies. In my revised version of the story, Icarus flies too high and falls into the ocean, but he survives, thrashing for a while beneath the waves while trying to recover his bearings before swimming to shore to start his life anew, with a greater understanding of the heights and depths of the human experience.

Re-visiting the road I have taken, through jails and hospitals, through depression and madness, through despair and elation, has brought light into the once-dark periods of my life; I can now view the crashing waves from the safety of the

G.H. Francis

shoreline. Living with a mental illness has taught me extreme tolerance of even the maddest ideas, because, even if I do not agree with another's opinions, who am I to say what reality is? Reality is a structureless concept. Reality is water within a pitcher. It seems constant and stable when inside the pitcher but, when poured into another vessel, it is easily reshaped and redefined. I have come to see that reality should not be a constant thing—it should be always changing, and only when the water within your pitcher freezes do real problems arise.

Two months prior to my third, and final, hospitalization I wrote:

### THE POTTER

One would think
The middle is the safest place

You stand there
safely observing
A single reality

the spinning wheel
pulls the fleshy clay
Distorting

Reality is something else
Now, a wider circle
A dizzier view
A different constellation
Or none at all

You take shape
with the presumption

that you've built this mold -
your *own* vessel

Glazed and fired
placed on a shelf
and sold


I believe the initial intention of this poem was to illustrate our personalities, which we create and harden before selling to others. It also discusses the variability of reality: the phrase, "Now, a wider circle," is a notion that stems from my experiences in madness, in which reality was changing from one moment to the next.

After the third hospitalization I returned to my parents' house and finally began taking my disorder, which had finally been diagnosed as schizoaffective disorder of the bipolar type, seriously. Due to the generosity of the State of Maryland, I was given free mental health care; without such a program I would probably be on the street yelling at street signs or scuttling sideways down your local boulevard, still believing myself a crustacean. I enrolled in a substance abuse program, which I attended weekly, hearing the stories of fellow addicts and learning about addictions of all types (emotional addiction, mental addiction, physical addiction, etc.). Once you understand something it is easier to overcome, and this knowledge, along with the weekly encouragement I received from fellow addicts, allowed me to stay on the wagon.

In addition to my addiction counseling, I also sought out the help of a psychiatrist and therapist—essential elements for managing a mental disorder. Therapists and psychiatrists are not the same. The psychiatrist is a medical doctor who ensures that I receive the proper medication. The trial-and-error process of finding the correct dosages and medications takes a long time, but I know it is necessary to stick with it and always take medication—always. Many people with mental disorders resign themselves to the notion that life is going to be miserable (as I did for seven years) and don't realize that a shift in their medication regiment can greatly increase their quality of life. My therapist is less medically focused, although she knows all about my medications. Her primary concern is helping me steer my life in the right direction. In the last few years my therapists have had to suffer through hours of rants about Kate, which no longer occur, and other minor issues that, if left untended, could grow out of control. I've also learned that it's crucial to be honest with my entire medical team, especially my therapists—if I lie to them about how I'm doing, then I'm really lying to myself, as well as denying myself care.

There are reminders of my manic episodes everywhere, especially in the words of particular songs I hear on the radio, and the occasional reminder at the clinic where I receive my treatment. On the bathroom wall above the urinal is written: *Ph'nglui mglw'nafh Cthulhu R'lyeh wgah'nagl fhtagn*, which means, "In his house at *R'lyeh*, dead Cthulhu waits dreaming." Cthulu is an evil deity from a short story entitled "The Call of Cthulu," by H.P. Lovecraft. From this short story, written in 1928, sprung a cult that is now centered in the Middle East but is also found in places throughout the United States. Cthulu came from the stars and has the ability to communicate with humans in their dreams. When I see things like this, I am reminded not only of my own manic episodes, but also that others are on their own journeys, probably frightened and hopeless, and desperately seeking a way out of their own nightmares.

Oftentimes individuals with bipolar or similar disorders feel that treatment takes away from their creative energy, but I know from experience that true creation is not a mad scribble of words on a page, one thing loosely connecting to another, but the contemplative, focused, and intentional development of a piece of art. As I learned in writing class, you can't just wait for inspiration to sweep you off your feet, you have to sit down in front of a computer, canvas, musical instrument, or any other creative outlet and work at it. It takes dedication—not madness—to create a great work. Although there are artists who fit the stereotype of the "creative genius," wild and unbridled by inhibitions and rules, these are few and far between, and allowing mania to control any aspect of your life is like jumping off a cliff in the dark, hoping, but not knowing, that there is water at the bottom.

This book was not intended to be merely the entertaining travails of a madman (although certain aspects may be just that) but also a source for educating those who wish to learn about mental disorders and a way of letting those with mental disorders know that they are not alone and, as long as they are willing to work at it, that they can manage their lives.

I was saving this for the end. It is the end of a piece written about my second hospitalization, added several years after the original text, which was previously written down in this book, was completed.

You decide, after trying to convince yourself that you can overcome this weakness, that you do have a disorder, and it won't heal, and this pain will be with you forever. Then you start over.

You start to understand that this isn't some sort of punishment, and you're not a pathetic creature, you're a person who must deal with a problem. Then you start to see other people with problems – the homeless man on crutches with plastic legs, the diabetic who has to stick needles in her finger every day, the obese man who has difficulty climbing a flight of stairs – and you realize that everyone has problems, and that maybe yours is not the most difficult to deal with. And you begin to understand poems such as this one by William Ernest Henley, which I first heard in the film of the same name:

### INVICTUS

Out of the night that covers me,
Black as the Pit from pole to pole,
I thank whatever gods may be
For my unconquerable soul.

In the fell clutch of circumstance
I have not winced nor cried aloud.
Under the bludgeonings of chance
My head is bloody, but unbowed.

Beyond this place of wrath and tears
Looms but the Horror of the shade,
And yet the menace of the years
Finds, and shall find, me unafraid.

It matters not how strait the gate,
How charged with punishments the scroll.
I am the master of my fate:
I am the captain of my soul.

And you decide to become the master of your fate, because it is a simple thing in the end: to take a few pills each day, to visit doctors, to avoid alcohol, to live healthily.

Soon you learn that the depth of a person's soul is measured not in how much they know, but in how great the pain they have experienced. And it is the distance between one's greatest happiness and one's greatest sadness that creates depth in a soul. For what soul can truly experience great happiness when it has not also experienced great pain?

With time and much hard work, the madness has receded. Some songs still bring me back. I hear them and wonder, "what if I was on the right track with those thoughts?" But these whims pass quickly and I brush them aside with a smile, gaining strength from the comparison between where I was and where I am now.

I take my pills every day and follow a fairly strict daily routine: 6-8 hours of work, 1 hour of watching news, 1 hour of practicing guitar, 2 hours of watching lectures or movies or television, 1 hour of writing, and 1 hour of reading. Aspects of this routine are often switched out for spending time with friends or family. Although I have been a member of an online dating site for several years with limited success, I continue to date women with the hope that I may one day fall in love again.

I am still recovering from Kate, or from the idea of Kate. This year is the first in 12 years that I did not email Kate on her birthday, although I did compose several emails without sending them. At times, I find myself composing an email to a woman I am dating and realize that the email is not really intended for her—it is intended for Kate. I suppose a part of me will always be writing to her; if not to her, to the green light shining across the bay.

I've found that the most difficult part of dating is telling the other person that I have a mental illness, and, to anyone reading this who has a mental illness, I have this advice: it's all in the delivery. If, when revealing your illness to another, you sit them down face-to-face and take on a somber tone, the other person will assume that this illness is a very serious thing. If, however, you mention it in passing ("Well, I'm schizoaffective, but I take meds and it's not really a big deal") you will have a far greater success rate—and don't do it on the very first date. Actually, this dating advice probably applies to everyone—we've all got different kinds of "baggage," be it bad break-ups or childhood trauma, and we don't need to share it on the very first date. The heavy details about hospitalizations, depression, etc. can come later, after they know who you are and see that you have this disorder under control.

I live in my own house and currently run two businesses, a writing/editing service and one of the top Internet marketing firms in Baltimore. I work from home and have three employees as well as eight freelancers who work for me.

Despite having come a very long way since my hospitalizations, I still have bad days, especially in the winter, during

ICARUS REDEEMED

which I am depressed and get little, if anything done. What I've learned is that sometimes you have to accept these days as unavoidable and get through them any way you can, knowing that the depression will end or, if it doesn't, that you have a plan to get help. It can be a vicious cycle to think, "normal people are out there working 9-to-5, why can't I? I'm just a lazy, worthless bum." There is a thin line between suffering from depression and just being lazy or apathetic, and knowing the difference becomes vital to overcoming difficult times. You may need one or two days to recover, or perhaps longer, but at some point you have to grit your teeth and pull out of it, knowing that you have the power overcome any obstacle, even depression. I have been through so many bouts of depression that I understand that the fastest way out of it, for me, is to do something productive, even if that's just an hour of work or taking the garbage to the curb. It takes strength, but once I show myself that I have the ability to fight my way through the sorrow, hope snowballs rapidly until the depression is gone.

Although one would never know just by meeting me, I do have a mental illness and that means I need to adjust my self-expectations. That means, as the recovering addict's Serenity Prayer says, "Accepting the things I cannot change and changing the things I can." I cannot change that I am depressed sometimes, but I can take my pills and know that the depression will end, and once it does I can be as productive as anyone else in this world.

I've also learned to accept my own capabilities and limitations. I am someone who experiences extreme anxiety in certain social situations, such as gatherings where I know few people and everyone is drinking. I challenge myself to participate in these scenarios, while accepting that at some point I may need to leave, even if it's still early in the evening. I will never be a social butterfly, and that's okay—that's not who I am.

Despite every possible effort, the stigma of mental illness continues to follow me in my life. Following yet another shooting in which the killer's mental state was called into question after having killed close family members, I was asked by a loved one, "You're not going to kill me, are you?" This was said half in jest, but there was a certain concern in their voice, and I realized that no matter what I do, some people will always fear that which is not known to them, and that which they cannot control. What many people don't understand is that mental illnesses *can* be controlled, with proper treatment and care. I believe it is society's responsibility to make sure people who need treatment can receive treatment; however, in the end it is the responsibility of those who have mental illnesses to manage their disorders. I feel empathy for killers with mental illness, wondering what would have happened had the wrong notion found its way into my mind during a severe manic episode. Although I never harmed anyone and I don't think I ever would, I understand the madness and I know that it leads you where it wants to go, not the other way around.

I now live a healthy and sane life, free from alcohol and drugs. I visit my psychiatrist regularly, and I keep a schedule. I believe these simple things are the key to living with any mental disorder. The disorder has made me strong, as strong as anyone I have ever met, and I would not trade it for anything else.

Nearly eight years to the day after I'd walked to Black Rocks in order to throw myself from the cliff face, I returned alone. Camped a few hundred meters from the rocks, this time intending to stay the evening, I stood in the spot that eight years prior was to be the last solid ground my feet would ever touch while I was still alive. I didn't want to pretend that that event never occurred; I wanted to face it head on and show I wasn't afraid.

It was a powerful moment, thinking of the eight years that had passed since then, of the people I'd met—my nephew and niece, and all the friends who have since come into my life. I thought of the sadness I could have caused and, overcome with emotion, I wept for some time. They were not tears of sorrow as they had been eight years prior; they were tears of joy. I was grateful for every moment experienced since that day, both good and bad.

It was during the previous winter, after another difficult breakup with a girlfriend, that I passed a cemetery and understood that any one of the individuals buried there would have given all their earthly wealth for just one more day to experience the sorrow I was then feeling. Reflecting on those eight years, I felt like I'd been given just that opportunity to rise up from my eternal slumber and experience the depth of pain and heights of happiness that life brings. Instead of one day, I had been granted eight years, and I still have many more to go. As if a cosmic sign, at that instant a shooting star fell to earth near the western horizon.

The same week I returned to the winding road I had so often traveled during those difficult days before and after my hospitalizations. It was as I had remembered it—lonely and silent—and nothing, not the smells nor the sounds, had changed, but I had.

The Buddhists say that you never step in the same river twice, and we are never the same from moment to moment. Each instant we are reborn. To change, we need only remove attachment from the past and move in whichever direction we choose. There is no looking back, because the past does not truly exist; there is only the present.

A therapist once told me about the tree at the end of life, one with red velvet pouches filled with individual persons' troubles hanging from the branches. At this tree each person is told they may hang their own pouch of troubles and exchange it with anyone else's. After circling the tree countless times, peeking into each pouch and finding lives with great trouble and lives with little trouble, everyone eventually returns to their own pouch, unties it from the tree, and enters the afterlife. In the end, our troubles make us who we are, and without them we wouldn't be ourselves; with them, we have the ability to form our troubles into whatever reality we wish to create. We are the masters of our own fate.

CPSIA information can be obtained at www.ICGtesting.com
Printed in the USA
BVOW06s2157150116

432753BV00011B/39/P